Workbook

그림으로 쉽게 이해되는 영어 문장 핵심 원리

한국식 영문법 말고

원어민식 그림

영문법

안 해 순 지음

워크북
한국식 영문법 말고 원어민식 그림 영문법

발 행 | 2024년 03월 25일
저 자 | 안해순
펴낸이 | 한건희
펴낸곳 | 주식회사 부크크
출판사등록 | 2014.07.15.(제2014-16호)
주 소 | 서울특별시 금천구 가산디지털1로 119 SK트윈타워 A동 305호
전 화 | 1670-8316
이메일 | info@bookk.co.kr

ISBN | 979-11-410-7737-2

www.bookk.co.kr

워크북
한국식
영문법
말고
원어민식
그림
영문법

안 해 순 지음

CONTENTS

Overview

Part 1. 원어민식 영문법 큰 그림

What are the fundamental rules in constructing a sentence?

문장을 구성하는 데 가장 기본이 되는 규칙은 뭘까?

문장의 규칙 즉 문법은 화자의 생각과 마음을 최대한 정확하고 간결하게 상대에게 전달하기 위해 언어 사용자들에게 주어진 최소한의 도구입니다. 그래서 영어 문법 규칙이 복잡하고 임의로 만들어진 게 절대 아닙니다. 영어 문법 규칙은 언어의 궁극적인 목표와 맞닿아 있기에 아주 명쾌하고 논리적입니다. 이 책에는 그 규칙을 누구든 쉽게 이해할 수 있도록 제시했습니다.

Are there any patterns among those various sentences?

다양한 문장 사이에 반복되는 패턴이 있을까?

다양한 영어 문장을 1~5형식으로 단순 범주화를 할 수 있을까요? 설령 어떤 문장이 몇 형식인지 안다고 해서 그 문장의 의미를 이해했다고 할 수 있을까요? 문장을 1~5형식으로 분류하는 것은 문장을 그저 피상적으로 보게 만들 뿐입니다. 그것으로는 길고 복잡한 문장의 구조를 절대로 정확히 알아낼 수 없습니다. 이 책에서 소개한 문장 선 그림 그리기(Sentence Diagramming)는 문장의 구조를 보다 입체적이고 정확하게 파악할 수 있게 합니다. 이 책은 영어 문장의 패턴을 한눈에 직관적으로 파악할 수 있도록 다양한 문장에 대한 선 그림 연습문제를 수록했습니다.

Part 2. 원어민식 영문법 쉬운 그림 나도 그림

What kinds of information does a verb contain? Shall we take it apart and look at the pieces?

동사는 어떤 정보들을 포함하고 있을까? 그걸 하나씩 떼어서 들여다볼까?

동사는 마치 여러 층의 재료를 쌓아 올린 햄버거와 같습니다. 동사는 여러 가지 정보를 압축하여 품고 있습니다. 동사가 품고 있는 각 층의 정보를 따로따로 떼어내어 이해하고 상황에 맞게 동사 형태를 바꿀 수 있어야 합니다. 이 책에 수록된 다양한 연습문제를 통해 상황과 의도에 맞게 동사 햄버거를 만들 수 있을 것입니다.

Can we visualize the structures of the complex sentences?

복잡한 문장의 구조를 시각화해서 볼 수 있을까?

문장 선 그림 그리기(Sentence Diagramming)는 문장의 의미를 정확하고 직관적으로 파악하기 위해 영어 원어민들이 쓰는 방식입니다. 이 책에 수록된 연습문제의 다양한 문장들을 직접 선 그림으로 그리며 문장 내 단어들의 의미 관계를 직관적으로 파악할 수 있을 것입니다.

Part 3. 원어민식 영문법 상상 그림

I'm not talking about the facts but my regret, my wish, and so on.

현실의 사실 말고 과거에 대한 후회, 현재의 바램, 미래의 소망, 그런 걸 말하는 거야.

영어 학습자들이 가장 힘들어하는 가정법의 핵심 원리를 그림으로 쉽게 설명했습니다. 이 책에 수록된 다양한 상황별 연습문제를 통해 여러분들도 과거의 후회, 현재의 바램, 미래의 소망 등을 영어로 정확히 표현할 수 있게 될 것입니다.

Preface

영어 문법의 가장 중요한 두 가지 요소는 문장 구조와 동사 형태입니다. <한국식 영문법 말고 원어민식 그림 영문법>에서는 그 두 가지 요소를 문장 선 그림(Sentence Diagramming)과 동사 햄버거 그림으로 각각 설명했습니다.

한국식 영문법은 문장을 1~5형식으로 분류하는 연습을 강조하는 편입니다. 하지만 그런 피상적인 연습만으로는 복잡하고 다양한 문장들의 의미를 제대로 간파할 수 없습니다. 문장 선 그림은 동사를 중심으로 문장의 의미 관계를 선 그림으로 그려 그 문장의 의미를 시각적으로 쉽게 이해하도록 해줍니다. 한편 동사 햄버거 그림은 동사가 품고 있는 정보를 낱낱이 떼어 이해하고 문맥과 상황에 따라 영어 동사의 형태를 정확히 변형시킬 수 있게 합니다.

<워크북 한국식 영문법 말고 원어민식 그림 영문법>에는 다양한 문장 선 그림 그리기 연습문제와 문맥과 문장에 따라 달라지는 영어 동사의 형태변형 연습문제가 수록되어 있습니다. 특히 이번 워크북에는 주교재에는 다루지 않은 가정법도 포함시켰습니다. 우리나라 학습자들이 가장 이해하기 어려워하는 가정법을 한눈에 파악할 수 있도록 그 원리를 도식화하고 문맥 속에서 가정법 문장의 동사 형태변형을 익힐 수 있도록 다양한 연습문제를 실었습니다.

이 책을 통해 여러분의 영어 자신감이 쑥쑥 커지길 바라며 여러분의 꿈을 펼치는 데 도움이 될 수 있기를 희망합니다.

2024년 봄,
안해순

Acknowledgements

<워크북 한국식 영문법 말고 원어민식 그림 영문법>은 현재 재직 중인 중학교의 학생들에게 실제 가르친 경험을 바탕으로 제작했습니다. 기존의 영어 문법 교육은 영어 문장 규칙에 대해 이유도 설명하지 않고 그저 학습자에게 암기를 강요한 방식이었습니다. 기존의 한국식 영문법으로 자신감과 흥미를 잃어버린 학생들에게 이 책은 영어 자신감을 심어주고 새로운 영어 문법의 세계를 알게 할 것입니다.

<한국식 영문법 말고 원어민식 그림 영문법>은 햄버거와 나뭇가지와 같은 시각적 도구를 활용해 영어 문법을 구체화, 시각화시켰습니다. 또한, 학습자에게 암기를 강요하며 막무가내로 규칙을 던져주는 영어 문법서가 아니라 규칙들을 관통하는 핵심 원리를 학습자들이 이해할 수 있도록 풀어서 설명한 '착한' 영어 문법서입니다.

이번에 출간한 <워크북 한국식 영문법 말고 원어민식 그림 영문법>은 원어민식 그림 영문법의 핵심 원리를 다양한 예문과 연습문제에 실제로 적용해 볼 수 있도록 제작했고 현재 재직 중인 중학교 방과 후 교육 활동 프로그램의 교재로 사용했습니다. 대부분 사람은 낯선 것에 대한 거부감을 가지기 마련입니다. 그게 학습해야 할 무엇이라고 하면 더욱 그러하지요. 그 방과 후 프로그램 참가 학생들에게도 '동사 햄버거'와 '영어 문장 선 그림'은 낯선 접근법이지만 기특하고 신기하게도 참가 학생들은 제 수업을 잘 따라와 주었습니다. 저를 믿고 한국식 영문법이 아닌 '원어민식 그림 영문법'이라는 새로운 방식을 끝까지 배운 학생들의 솔직한 후기입니다.

> 문장을 그림으로 그려보면서 영어 문장을 봤을 때 문법적으로만 생각하는 것이 아니라 머리속으로 그림을 그려 더 쉽게 구조화할 수 있게 되었다.

> 문법 용어를 어렵게 사용하지 않고 쉽게 풀어서 수업하니까 더 잘 와닿게 되었다.

> - 문장의 구조를 선그림으로 그린 것
> - 문장을 볼 때 항상 몇 형식인지 먼저 봤는데 문장 그림이라는 것을 배우면서 문장의 구조를 이렇게 간단하고 쉽게 볼 수 있다는 것을 깨달았다. 앞으로 해석하기 어려운 문장을 보면 이 방법을 이용할 수 있을 것 같다.

> 문법을 어렵지 않게 알려 주셔서 좋았습니다.

> 동사 햄버거 모양이 이해하기 쉬웠어서 도움이 되었다. 선 그림으로 그려서 주어나 동사 등 보는데 도움이 되었다.

> 학기 중에 동영상을 통해서 선과 방식이 문장을 당겨진 수 있게 되었고
> 이후에 나문장 해석에도 도움이 될 것 같다

> 작년에는 무작정 외우기만 했던 것을 알기 쉽게 이해하기 쉽게
> 설명해주신게 특히 좋았다

> 문장의 전체적인 구조, 왜 이렇게 될수 밖에 없는가를 달러 국서서 오래 기억에 남을거같다
> (ex)왜 hope가 으면 위에 to가 온다

> 문장의 구조를 선그림으로 그린 것, 문장의 구조를 보니 긴 문장이라도 해석이 될수
> 있어서 입니다

> 문장 구조 선그림이 많이 도움이 되었다 전에는 긴문장을 보면 어디서 부터 해석해야 하는지 감을 못잡았
> 있는데 이제는 선그림으로 그려 문장을 확실하게 파악할 수 있다

> 1번에서 말해둣이 문장의 구조를 선그림으로 그린 20/5증이 25에 된 것
> 같다 항상 문장을 보면 돌린 부분을 찾는 게 어려웠는데 이번 수업을 통해
> 선 그림으로 이해해 찾을 수 있었기 때문이다

"낯선 개념이지만 기특하게도 너무 잘 이해하고 선생님을 믿고 끝까지 잘 배워줘서 고맙다~."

학생들의 놀라운 성과와 긍정적인 피드백 덕분에 '한국식 영문법 말고 원어민식 그림 영문법'에 대한 확신이 생겼습니다. <워크북 한국식 영문법 말고 원어민식 그림 영문법>으로 더 많은 학습자들이 혼자서도 쉽게 영어 문장의 핵심 원리를 익힐 수 있었으면 합니다.

▌생각을 영어 문장으로 변환할 때 기억해야 할 것들

1. 한 문장에는 꼭 (주어), (동사)는 하나씩 와야 한다.

모든 문장은 '누가 무엇을 하다' 또는 '누가 무엇이다'라는 뼈대를 가진다.

Subject ‥‥‥‥ Verb ‥‥‥‥ .

  (주어: 누가)   (동사: ~이다/~하다)

Q. 왜 각 문장에는 주어와 동사가 와야 할까?

A. 그래야 시간 효율이 높은 대화가 될 테니까.

연습문제 1.

다음 문장에서 동사를 찾아 세모 하시오.

① I'll give you my apple.

② No other boy in the world can paint as well as me.

③ Tom agreed with a long face, but with a joyous heart.

④ Tom came outside with a can of white paint and a brush.

⑤ Christmas is an important time for sharing and celebration.

2. 메세지를 문장 단위로 끊어서 전해야 한다. (마침표)는 문장의 끝을 나타낸다.

S(주어) 한 개..... V(동사) 한 개.....(마침표)/
S(주어) 한 개..... V(동사) 한 개.....(마침표)/

> Q. 왜 그럴까?
> A. 한 번에 하나씩 줘야 정리가 쉬우니까. 한 번에 한 문장 단위로 생각을 뱉어내야, 쉽게 정리될 테니까.

연습문제 2.

다음 이어진 문장들을 문장 단위로 끊어서 마침점 위치에 V표 하시고 다음 문장의 첫 단어는 대문자로 바꾸시오.

①

When the day is over, I return home I share stories from my day with my family over a delicious dinner afterward, I might watch TV, read a book, or spend time on hobbies it's a peaceful time to unwind and reflect on the events of the day

②

Friends are special people who make me happy we play together, share secrets, and help each other when we're sad having good friends makes life more fun and enjoyable

③

Mark Twain is one of the America's best-loved writers his novels, especially The Adventures of Tom Sawyer(1876) and The adventures of Huckleberry Finn (1885), are still very popular

S(주어) .... V(동사) ... 딱풀(접속사) S(주어) .....V(동사) .....(마침표)

(예문) I opened the window **because** it was very hot.

Q. 왜 그럴까?

A. 복잡한 생각들을 짧은 직선으로 그리다 보면 조각, 조각이 너무 많아진다.

우리 뇌는 낱개로 존재하는 데이터를 묶음 처리하거나 압축해서 낱개 데이터를 최소화하고 싶어 한다. 관련 있는 조각을 묶어서 말해주면 듣는 사람이 더 편하게 메시지를 처리하게 된다.

연습문제 3.

다음 문장에서 접속사 (딱풀)을 네모 하시오.

① I buy it although I don't need it.

② Before you go shopping, make a shopping list.

③ If you set a goal for yourself, it will be easier to limit your spending.

④ In sports, only the players get a trophy, but they don't win on their own.

⑤ Changing the tires is especially important because the tires wear out easily in a high speed race.

4. 각 문장의 주인공인 주어, 동사를 방해해서는 안 된다.

동사와 비슷하게 생긴 말들은 형태를 바꿔서 주인공 동사의 앞길에 방해되지 않게 해야 한다.

(예문) Joe washed cars <u>to make</u> money.

　　　주어(누가)? Joe　/ 동사 (뭘 했다)? washed

make (벌다)는 동사(주인공)가 아니니, 다른 옷을 입어야 한다. 여기선 to make라는 옷으로 바꿔 입었다.

Q. 왜 조연들은 옷을 바꿔 입어야 할까?

A. 주어, 동사가 제일 중요한 정보니까, 조연은 눈에 덜 띄어야 하니까.

연습문제 4.

다음 문장에서 조연(동사가 형태변형을 한 것)을 동그라미 하시오.

① I like to buy things on sale.

② Buying things on sale is good.

③ They are designed to work for humans.

④ You can save money faster to buy the ticket.

⑤ By following the rule, you can manage your money better.

▌영어 문장에 관한 핵심

✎ 하나의 문장 (마침표로 표시) 안에는 주어가 1개, 동사 1개만 와야 함.

S (주어) ....V (동사)................................(마침표)

주어 1개, 동사 1개가 와야 함.

✎ 동사는 시간 정보(과거, 현재, 미래)를 품어야 함.

✎ 주어와 동사가 각 문장의 핵심 주인공이기에 주어와 동사를 정확히 파악하는 게 중요.

✎ 문장의 핵심 내용은 주어, 동사, 목적어, 보어(주어나 목적어를 보충해주는 말) 안에 있음.

✎ 나머지 내용은 which one (어느 것?), when, where, how와 관련된 세부 사항

[한 눈에 딱! 문장 구조 알게 그림]

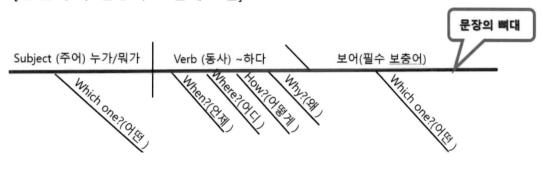

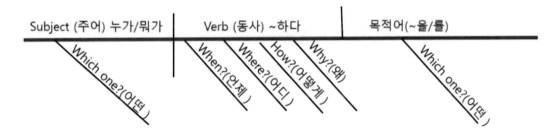

<예시 1> The king is here.

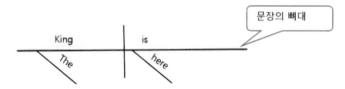

<예시 2> The king is kind.

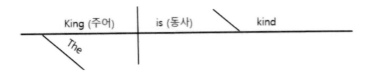

<예시 3> The king is a genius.

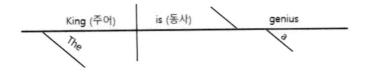

<예시 4> We are studying English grammar.

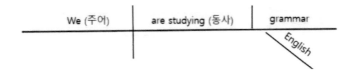

<예시 5> We looked up the word.

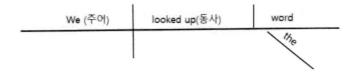

<예시 6> The teacher gave everyone a chocolate cookie.

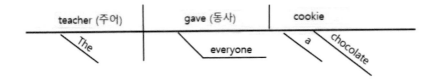

<예시 7> The teacher gave a chocolate cookie to everyone.

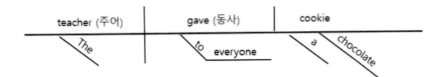

<예시 8 > The students bowed respectfully to their English teacher.

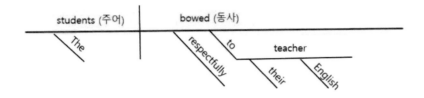

<예시 9> The king considered the tall man honest.

다음 문장들을 선 그림(Diagramming)으로 그리시오.

① He speaks softly.

② She runs quickly.

③ They dance gracefully.

④ The wind blows gently.

⑤ The dog barks loudly.

⑥ The baby giggles happily.

⑦ A big dog was in the yard.

⑧ The sun shines brightly.

⑨ The flowers bloom beautifully.

⑩ The cat is sleeping peacefully.

다음 문장들을 선 그림(Diagramming)으로 그리시오

① He feels sad.

② They are tired.

③ The flowers smell good.

④ She seems his favorite child.

⑤ She is happy with her new job.

⑥ The laptop on the table is broken.

⑦ He is proud of his achievement.

⑧ We are worried about the test tomorrow.

⑨ They are disappointed with the results.

⑩ She has been angry with us for three days.

다음 문장들을 선 그림(Diagramming)으로 그리시오.

① They ate a delicious meal.

② I bought a beautiful dress.

③ He watched a thrilling movie.

④ She reads an interesting book.

⑤ The cat caught a small mouse.

⑥ We visited a fascinating museum.

⑦ We attended a cheerful birthday party.

⑧ She wrote a heartfelt letter to her friend.

⑨ The students solved a difficult math problem.

⑩ She reads a fascinating book quietly in the cozy corner.

다음 문장들을 선 그림(Diagramming)으로 그리시오.

① They sent me a funny video.

② I bought my sister a stylish dress.

③ She gave her friend a thoughtful gift.

④ They lent their neighbor a helping hand.

⑤ She wrote her boyfriend a heartfelt letter.

⑥ He showed his parents a beautiful painting.

⑦ He offered the children some tasty treats.

⑧ We showed our friends a new workout routine.

⑨ The waiter brought the customers a delicious meal.

⑩ We handed the teacher our completed assignments.

다음 문장들을 선 그림(Diagramming)으로 그리시오.

① They called him a hero.

② She painted the wall blue.

③ They named the baby Ethan.

④ The jury declared him guilty.

⑤ I find the movie entertaining.

⑥ We made her the team captain.

⑦ We made him captain of the team.

⑧ She considers him a talented musician.

⑨ He appointed her his personal assistant.

⑩ The committee declared the project a success.

▌ 문장의 주인공: 동사

모든 생각은 '~가~하다' '~가 ~이다'의 문장으로 정리된다.

즉, 생각의 핵심은 주어와 동사로 이루어져 있다.

   S   ......   V.......   (마침표)

  Subject (주어)   Verb (동사)

  누가   ~하다/~이다

▌ 동사: 4가지 정보의 압축파일

1) 동사 자체의 행동(base) : 행위 그 자체

2) 언제 (tense)   : 과거/현재/미래

3) 양상(aspect)   : 특정 기간 동안 쭈욱 / 순간 진행 중

4) 가함/당함 (voice)   : 가함/ 당함

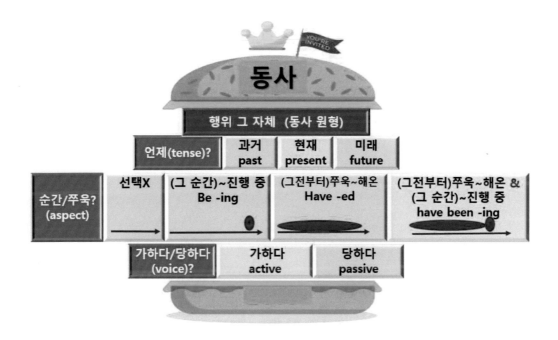

괄호 속 동사를 알맞게 바꾸시오.

① I _____ (watch) a movie yesterday.

② They ___ (have) a picnic last summer.

③ We ____ (read) a book yesterday evening.

④ She _____ (clean) her room last weekend.

⑤ The dog _____ (bark) loudly this morning.

⑥ She ___ (eat) dinner at a restaurant last night.

⑦ She _____ (visit) her grandparents two days ago.

⑧ He _____ (study) English for two hours yesterday.

⑨ They _____ (play) soccer in the park last Saturday.

⑩ My family _____ (travel) to the beach last summer.

괄호 속 동사를 알맞게 바꾸시오

① The cat is _____ (sleep) all day.

② I am _____ (read) a book right now.

③ She is _____ (eat) lunch at the moment.

④ He is _____ (watch) a movie on TV now.

⑤ They _____ (play) soccer in the park now.

⑥ She _____ (write) a letter to her friend now.

⑦ They _____ (study) English this morning.

⑧ He _____ (listen) to music in the afternoon.

⑨ I _____ (play) video games at the moment.

⑩ We _____ (study) English grammar this very moment.

▌ (그전부터) 쭉 해 온 : have/has -ed

과거에서 현재까지 그 기간 사이에 일어난 일, 경험 또는 완료된 일

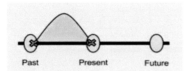

Duration from the past until now

【I <u>have lived</u> in Daegu for 5 years.】

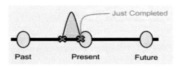

Recent action just completed

【I <u>have</u> just <u>finished</u> my homework.】

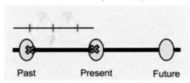

Repeated Events in the past **until now**

【I <u>have been</u> to Jejudo 3 times.】

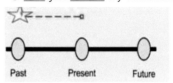

Recent action with present result

【I <u>have lost</u> my wallet.】

연습문제 3.

괄호 속 동사를 알맞게 바꾸시오.

① I _____ (lose) my keys. I need to search the house. I hope I find them soon.

② We _____ (lose) our way. Let's ask for directions. I hope we find the right path.

③ She _____ (visit) Paris once. She traveled to Paris last year and enjoyed exploring the Eiffel Tower.

④ We _____ (study) French for two semesters. We have practiced speaking French with our classmates.

⑤ He _____ (lose) his phone. He remembers having it in the car. He needs to retrace his steps.

⑥ I started my homework in the afternoon. I _____ (finish) my homework. I feel relieved now that it's done.

⑦ He _____ (study) English for five years. He started learning English in high school. He can now speak fluently and confidently.

⑧ I _____ (live) in this city for three years. I moved here after finishing college. I have made many friends during my time here.

⑨ He _____ (know) her since childhood. They grew up in the same neighborhood. He has always been a good friend to her.

⑩ She _____ (work) at that company since last month. She enjoys her job and the work environment. She has learned a lot of new skills in her role.

▌ (그전부터) 쭈욱 해 온 & 지금도 ~하는 중: have/has been ing

너는 지금까지 쭈욱 돈을 쓰고 있어 너무 많이.

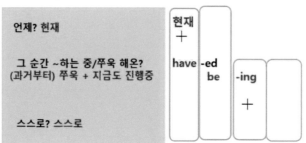

have been spending

You have been spending too much.

연습문제 4.

괄호 속 동사를 알맞게 바꾸시오.

① She _____ (study) for the exam all week. She is feeling a bit stressed.

② They _____ (play) in the park for hours. They are getting tired and hungry.

③ He _____ (work) on his project since yesterday. He is excited to see the final result.

④ They _____ (clean) the house all day. It looks neat and tidy now.

⑤ He _____ (exercise) regularly. He is feeling healthier and more energetic.

⑥ I _____ (read) this book for days. It's a captivating story, and I can't put it down.

⑦ We _____(wait) for the train since morning. We are getting impatient as it is delayed.

⑧ He _____ (learn) to play the guitar for a year. He can now play several songs confidently.

⑨ I _____ (wait) for my friend at the coffee shop. She is running late, and I am getting worried.

⑩ I _____ (practice) their English conversation skills since I was 10, and I feel more comfortable speaking in English now.

▌ 과거 특정 시점부터 과거 특정 시점까지 쭈욱 해 온 : had ‒ed

▶ 【 have/has+ ~ed 】   vs.   【 had+ ~ed 】   vs.   【~ed 】

I **have lived** in Daegu for 5 years.   I **had lived** in Daegu for 5 years when I **entered** the college.

【 have/has+ ~ed 】 5년전부터 지금까지	**【 had+ ~ed 】** 과거 【~ed】 그 이전 5년간 대학교 입학

▶ 【 had+ ~ed 】

쓰임: 과거에 일어난 두 가지 일 중 **먼저 일어난 일을 명확하게 할 때** 씀.

형태: 「**had + ~ed (과거분사)**」

e.g. When I **arrived** there, the show **had** already **started**.

         ② 나중에 일어남   ① 먼저 일어남

(**둘 다 이미 일어난 일**   )

연습문제 5.

괄호 속 동사를 알맞게 바꾸시오.

① She ___ never ____ (see) snow until last year.

② Tom _____ (go) out when I visited his house.

③ I _____ (live) with my parents until I was 20.

④ Jack told me that he ___ never ____ (see) a parrot.

⑤ He ___ just ____ (take) a bath when the phone rang.

⑥ I _____ (finish) my homework before I went to bed.

⑦ I ___ never ____ (try) Mexican food before I visited Mexico.

⑧ I got upset when I found I _____ (leave) my car key in the car.

⑨ When I dropped by his office yesterday, he _____ (go) to the bank.

⑩ He _____ (study) English for three years before he moved to an English-speaking country.

▌ 당하는 : be -ed

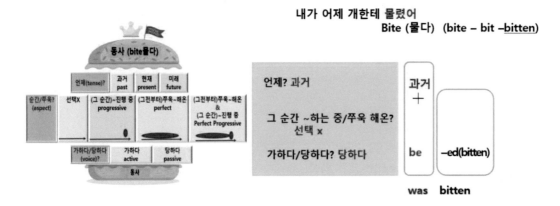

내가 어제 개한테 물렸어
Bite (물다) (bite – bit –bitten)

I was bitten by a dog yesterday.

연습문제 6.

괄호 속 동사를 알맞게 바꾸시오.

① The letter _____ (write) by Sarah. It has important information.

② The letter _____ (write) by my sister. She has excellent writing skills.

③ The message _____ (send) by mistake. We need to clarify the situation.

④ The new bridge _____ (build) last year. It connects the two neighborhoods.

⑤ The report _____ (prepare) by the team. It is ready for the presentation.

⑥ The film _____ (direct) by a famous filmmaker. It received positive reviews.

⑦ The movie _____ (watch) by a large audience. It has become a box office hit.

⑧ The book _____ (read) by many people. It has received positive reviews from readers. The book _ often _____(recommend) by teachers

⑨ The meal _____ (cook) by a professional chef. The chef takes pride in creating delicious dishes. The meal _____ (serve) in a beautifully decorated restaurant.

⑩ The car _____ (wash) by the car-wash employees. They ensure that every part of the car is clean. The car _____ (dry) and polished after the wash.

▌ 당하고 있는 중 : be being ‒ed

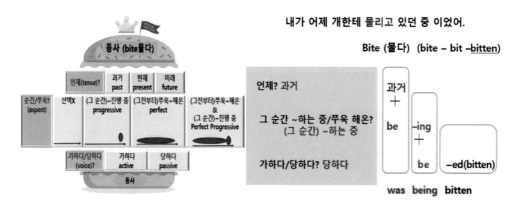

내가 어제 개한테 물리고 있던 중 이었어.

Bite (물다) (bite ‒ bit ‒bitten)

was being bitten

I was being bitten by a dog.

괄호 속 동사를 알맞게 바꾸시오.

① The project _____ (work) on by the team. They are collaborating and sharing ideas. The deadline is approaching, so they are working diligently.

② The car _____(repair) at the mechanic's shop. They are fixing the engine issue. The brakes are being checked(check) for any problems.

③ The letter _____ (write) by my friend. She is using beautiful stationery for the letter. The letter is being addressed and will be sent soon.

④ The garden _____ (plant) by the volunteers. They are using seeds and tools. The community event is just around the corner, so they are working hard.

⑤ The event _____ (organize) by the committee. They are coordinating logistics and inviting guests. The big day is coming soon, so they are staying focused.

⑥ The cake _____ (bake) by the baker. They are using fresh ingredients. The celebration is tonight, so they are making sure everything is perfect.

⑦ The experiment _____ (conduct) by the scientists. They are using advanced equipment. The results are expected soon, so they are staying attentive.

⑧ The website _____ (develop) by the IT team. They are coding and testing. The launch is next week, so they are working meticulously.

⑨ The lesson _____ (teach) by the teacher. They are using interactive methods. The exam is next week, so they are ensuring students understand the material.

⑩ The report _____ (write) by the journalist. They are interviewing sources and gathering information. The deadline is tight, so they are working diligently.

▌ 쭈욱~당하고 있는 중 : have been being -ed

내가 5분째 개한테 물리고 있는 중 이야.

I have been being bitten by a dog for 5 minutes.

연습문제 8.

괄호 속 동사를 알맞게 바꾸시오.

① The report _____ (review) by the supervisor for the past hour. Important suggestions have been made for improvement.

② The new software _____ (test) by the IT department all week. They have identified a few bugs that need fixing.

③ The novel _____ (read) by book club members over the last month. Everyone has been sharing their favorite parts during meetings.

④ The emails _____ (answer) by the customer service team since morning. They have successfully addressed most customer inquiries.

⑤ The cookies _____ (bake) by the chef for the last half hour. The delightful aroma has been filling the entire kitchen.

⑥ The house _____ (paint) by the workers throughout the summer. The fresh colors have completely transformed its appearance.

⑦ The song _____ (sing) by the choir during rehearsals this week. They have perfected the harmonies for the upcoming performance.

⑧ The lessons _____ (teach) by the teacher for the entire semester. Students have been actively participating and learning new concepts.

⑨ The repairs _____ (make) on the car for the past few days. The mechanic has finally fixed the engine issue.

⑩ The updates _____ (implement) by the IT team over the last month. Users have noticed improvements in the system's performance.

▌효율적 의사전달의 제일 중요한 약속!

한 문장에 주어 하나, 동사 하나!!

다음을 영어 문장으로 써보자.

내가 끝냈어 (finish)개 산책시키는 걸(walk).

> Q. 문장에 행위를 나타내는 말(동사)이 두 개나 필요한데 어떻게 하죠?
>
> A. 행위를 나타내는 말(동사)을 다 사용해도 된다.
>
> 다만 시간의 정보 (과거 -ed /현재 -es / 미래 will)는 문장 전체의 동사만 품게 해야 한다.
>
> 대체로 우리말로 번역할 때 맨 마지막에 오는 동사가 문장 전체의 동사가 된다.
>
> 나머지 동사들은 다른 모양(to 동사원형/ 동사원형ing/동사원형)으로 바꿔줘야 한다.

나는 개 산책 시키는 걸 <u>끝냈어</u>.

맨 끝에 오는 '끝냈어'라는 동사만 주인공 동사로 시간의 정보를 품도록 하면 된다.

I finished walking a dog.

> Q. 그런데, 왜 한 문장에 시간의 정보(tense)를 메인 동사 하나만 품도록 할까?
>
> A. 시간에 대한 정보를 동사 하나가 대표로 전한다. 같은 문장에 쓰인 다른 준동사(verbals)가
> 계속 시간의 정보를 말할 필요가 없다. 효율을 높여야 한다. 반복을 없애야 하기 때문이다.

▌동사 : 시간의 정보(tense) 있음.

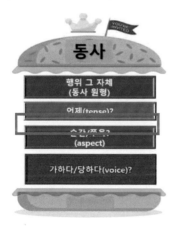

동사는 4가지 정보의 압축파일이다.

▌준동사(verbals) : 시간의 정보 (tense) 없음.

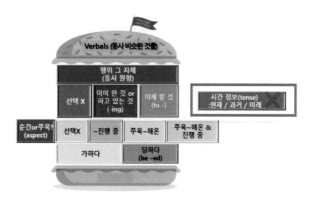

▌잠깐! 오늘의 핵심 Verbals 세 가지 메뉴 각각 맛보기

> ❶ -ing (동사원형ing) : 이미 한 것이나 지금 하는 행위를 담음/ 일반적인 행위 자체
> ❷ to- (to 동사원형) : 이제 할 행위를 담음 / 이제 곧 할 구체적인 행위
> ❸ 선택 X (동사원형) : 행위 그 자체 기본 뜻만 담백하게 담음
> 　　　　　　　　　　　시키다(let, make, have) 동사/ 감각 동사(see, hear...)

❶ -ing : 이미 한 것이나 지금 하고 있는 행위를 담음

　예를 들어, '나는 개 산책시키는 걸 끝냈어.'라는 문장이 있다고 하자. 이 문장에서 주인공은 '내가(주어)', '끝냈어 (동사)'이다. 여기에서 행동을 나타내는 말은 두 개가 있다.

> • 끝내다 (finish): 문장 전체의 주인공 – 주인공 동사(Verb)
> • 산책시키다 (walk): 부수적 정보를 전하는 조연 –준동사(Verbal)

'끝냈어'를 기준으로 '개 산책시키는 행동'은 이미 일어난 행동이므로 '-ing'를 붙여서 동사 충돌을 막는다.

위의 예문에 적용하면 노란 체크 표시가 된 부분을 가져다가 형태를 조합하면 된다.

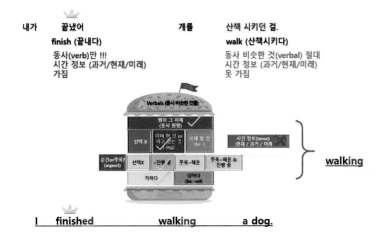

'나는 개 산책시키는 걸 끝냈어'라는 문장은 'I finished walking a dog.' 이 된다.

▌보충 설명 ①

Q. 왜 전치사 뒤에는 반드시 '동사원형ing'만 써야 할까?

◉ 아래 예문의 ( ) 안에 들어갈 말은?

I am good at (swimming/ to swim).

☞ 정답은 swimming.

전치사(in, on, at, of, to.....) 뒤에는 'to 동사 원형'이 오면 전치사가 겹치는 것을 막기 위해 전치사 뒤에는 '동사 원형ing'를 쓴다.

▌보충 설명 ②

Q. 왜 어떤 동사는 '동사원형ing'와 'to 동사원형' 둘 다 쓸까? 각각의 뜻 차이가 있을까?

◉ 아래 각 예문의 (watch)의 알맞은 형태는?

(1) A: What's your hobby?

    B: I like (watch) movies.   ☞ 정답은 watching.

(2) A: What shall we do this afternoon?

    B: I'd like (watch) a movie.   ☞ 정답은 to watch

'to watch'는 지금 곧 하려는 구체적인 행동을 의미하지만 'watching'은 일반적으로 영화 보는 행동 자체를 의미함.

괄호 속 동사를 알맞게 바꾸시오.

① I **enjoy** _____ (swim) in the pool.

② I have **given up** _____ (lose) weight.

③ Suddenly, we **stopped** _____(talk).

④ He **likes** _____ (run) long distances.

⑤ Sorry to **keep** you _____ (wait) so long.

⑥ We **practice** _____ (speak) English every day.

⑦ We **appreciate** _____ (receive) thoughtful gifts.

⑧ He tried to **avoid** _____ (answer) my question.

⑨ She is good **at** _____ (play) the piano.

⑩ He is interested **in** _____ (learn) new languages.

▌❷ to- : 이제 할 행위를 담음

예를 들어, '내가 결심했어 개를 산책시키기로 매일'이라는 문장이 있다고 하자. 이 문장에서 주인공은 '내가(주어)', '결심했어 (동사)'이다. 여기에서 행동을 나타내는 말은 두 개가 있다.

- 결심하다 (decide) : 문장 전체의 뼈대가 되는 주인공–주인공 동사(Verb)
- 산책시키다 (walk) : 문장 내 부수적 정보를 전하는 조연 – 동사 비슷한 것 (Verbals)

위의 예문에 적용하면 노란 체크 표시가 된 부분을 가져다가 형태를 조합하면 된다.

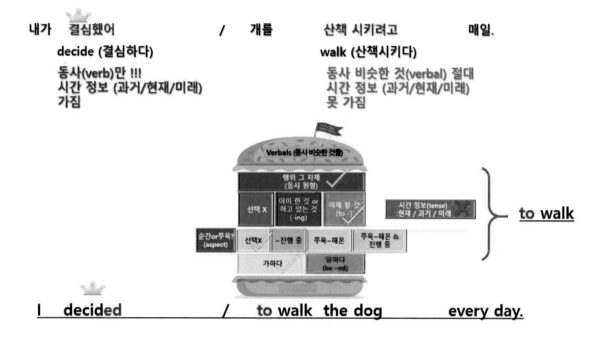

'결심했어'(메인 동사/주인공)를 기준으로 '개 산책시키는 행동'은 이제 일어날 행동이므로 –to를 붙여서 동사 충돌을 막는다.

괄호 속 동사를 알맞게 바꾸시오.

① I **agreed** _____ (help) him.

② I **promised** not _____ (be) late.

③ I **hope** _____ (find) a new job soon.

④ They can't **afford** _____ (buy) a house.

⑤ We **decided** _____ (take) a taxi home.

⑥ He **needs**_____ (finish) his homework.

⑦ Her dream **is** _____ (make) a movie.

⑧ He **promises** _____ (help) with the project.

⑨ We **plan** _____ (visit) the museum tomorrow.

⑩ We **aim** _____ (improve) our English skills.

▌❸ 선택 X : 행위 그 자체 기본 뜻만 담백하게 담음

예를 들어, '내가 시켰어 그에게 개를 산책시키라고 매일'이라는 문장이 있다고 하자. 이 문장에서 주인공은 '내가(주어)', '시켰어 (동사)'이다. 여기에서 행동을 나타내는 말은 두 개가 있다.

- 시키다 (make)　　 : 문장 전체의 뼈대가 되는 주인공 – 주인공 동사(Verb)
- 산책시키다 (walk): 부수적 정보를 전하는 조연 – 동사 비슷한 것 (Verbal)

위의 예문에 적용하면 노란 체크 표시가 된 부분을 가져다가 형태를 조합하면 된다.

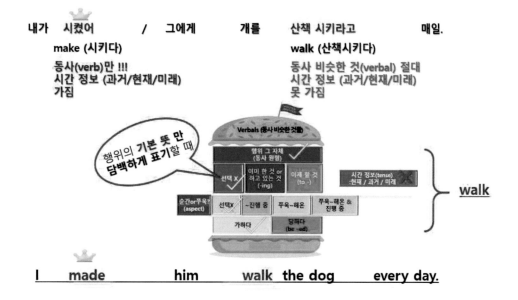

1) 주로 '시키다' 동사(사역동사: let, make, have)가 이 패턴을 쓴다.

2) 지각 동사(see, notice, hear, feel, listen to, smell)도 동사 원형 쓰지만, 그 순간의 진행 상태임을 강조하기 위해서는 '-ing'를 쓰기도 한다.

보충 설명

Q. 지각 동사 뒤 '동사원형'인 경우와 '동사원형ing'인 경우 어떤 의미 차이가 있을까?

◉ 아래 각 예문에 들어갈 'walk'의 알맞은 형태는?

(1) I saw you (walk) a dog, but I was on my way to work in a hurry.

(2) I saw you (walk) a dog until you turned the corner.

☞ (1) 정답은 walking : 그 순간을 보았음. 서둘러 일하러 가는 길에 잠시 보았다는 의미.
(2) 정답은 walk : 전 과정을 보았음. 코너를 돌 때까지 계속 보고 있었음을 의미.

연습문제 3.

괄호 속 동사를 알맞게 바꾸시오.

① **Let** me _____(read) the letter.

② I **saw** him ___ (fall) off the wall.

③ I have never **seen** her _____ (dance).

④ Did you **notice** anyone ___ (go) out?

⑤ Please **let** me _____ (know) if you need any assistance.

⑥ **Let** the children ____ (play) in the park for a while.

⑦ Can you **hear** the music _____ (play) in the background?

⑧ The challenging puzzle will **make** you _____ (think) critically.

⑨ **Let** me ____ (take) you out for dinner to celebrate your success.

⑩ My parents always **make** me___ (do) my homework before I go out.

▌ 한 문장에 동사 두 개 충돌 해결법: to 동사원형

Q. 다음 예시 문장처럼, 한 문장에 행위를 의미하는 단어 즉, 동사가 여러 개 올 수도 있다.
   이 경우 어떻게 동사 충돌을 해결할 수 있을까? 다음 문장을 영어로 옮겨 보자.
   <예시1> 그는 매일 아침 살을 빼려고 조깅한다.

A. 이 문장에서 행동을 의미하는 단어는 2개 (조깅한다, 뺀다)이다.
   한 문장에 이렇게 행동이 2개 나오면, 그 중에 주인공 동사 (보통 우리말로 번역된 문장의 마지막에
   오는 단어)는 그대로 유지 시키고, 나머지 행동을 나타내는 동사를 'to 동사원형'이나
   '동사원형 ing'로 바꾸면 된다.

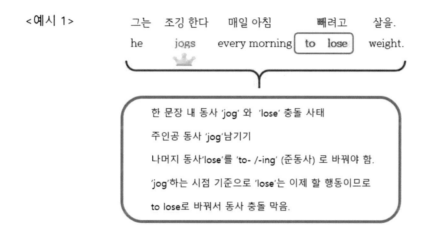

<예시 2> We must find a way to be successful.

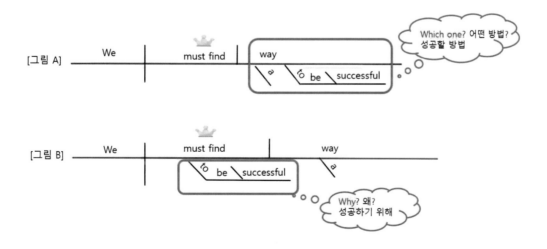

<예시 3> He washed cars every morning <u>to make money</u>.

그는 세차했다 매일 아침/ 돈을 벌려고.

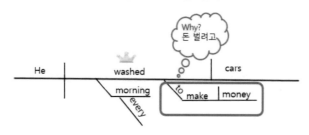

<예시 4> He continues <u>to eat lots of cakes</u>.

그는 계속 한다/ 먹는 것을 /많은 케익을.

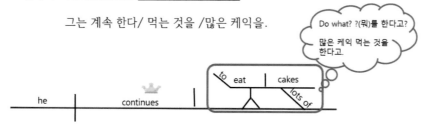

<예시 5> <u>To lose weight</u> is his goal.

살 빼는 것이 그의 목표이다.

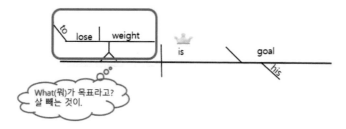

<예시 6> The best coffee <u>to drink</u> is this blend of two flavors.

마실 최고의 커피는 이 두 가지 향을 섞은 거다.

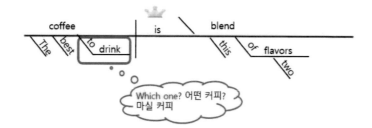

다음 문장들을 선 그림(Diagramming)으로 그리시오.

① They exercised regularly to stay fit.

② We saved money to buy a new car.

③ She woke up early to catch the bus.

④ They studied hard to pass the exam.

⑤ He works diligently to achieve his goals.

⑥ I practiced daily to improve my guitar skills.

⑦ He waited patiently to meet his favorite celebrity.

⑧ She ate a healthy breakfast to start her day right.

⑨ The children played outside to enjoy the sunshine.

⑩ We cleaned the house thoroughly to prepare for guests.

다음 문장들을 선 그림(Diagramming)으로 그리시오.

① She has a book to read.

② She has a puzzle to solve.

③ He wants a toy to play with.

④ She needs a chair to sit on.

⑤ I bought a brush to paint with.

⑥ The cat needs a bowl to eat from.

⑦ He has a bike to ride in the park.

⑧ She purchased a laptop to work on.

⑨ She bought a dress to wear to the party.

⑩ The students have textbooks to study from.

다음 문장들을 선 그림(Diagramming)으로 그리시오.

① They love to travel.

② I hope to find a new job soon.

③ He needs to finish his homework.

④ They decided to go on a vacation.

⑤ Her dream is to make a movie.

⑥ The dog loves to chase after the ball.

⑦ He promises to help with the project.

⑧ We aim to improve our English skills.

⑨ We plan to visit the museum tomorrow.

⑩ They like to eat ice cream in the summer.

▌ 한 문장에 동사 두 개 충돌 해결법 : 동사원형ing

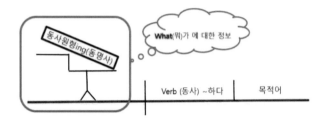

<예시 1> 한밤중에 커피 마시는 것은 수면 장애를 일으킨다.

맨 끝에 오는 '일으킨다'라는 동사만 주인공 동사로 시간의 정보를 품도록 하면 된다.

Drinking coffee at midnight causes sleep problems.

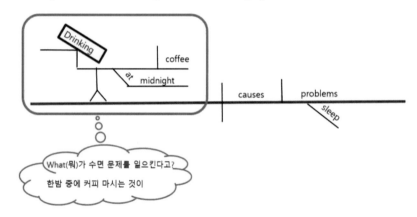

<예시 2> 나는 개 산책시키는 일을 끝냈다.

맨 끝에 오는 '끝냈다'라는 동사만 주인공 동사로 시간의 정보를 품도록 하면 된다.

I finished walking a dog.

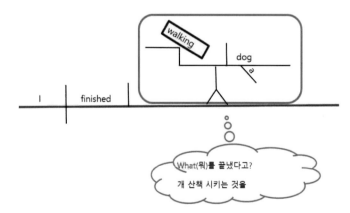

다음 문장들을 선 그림(Diagramming)으로 그리시오.

① I like painting pictures.

② I enjoy swimming in the pool.

③ He dislikes running long distances.

④ She is good at playing the piano.

⑤ They like playing soccer after school.

⑥ We practice speaking English every day.

⑦ She loves dancing to her favorite songs.

⑧ We appreciate receiving thoughtful gifts.

⑨ He is interested in learning new languages.

⑩ He prefers reading novels over watching TV.

▌ 접속사 (딱풀, 연결체인)

두 개의 낱개 문장을 하나의 문장으로 붙일 때는 반드시 접착제(접속사)가 필요하다.

Kristin watered a sunflower   , and   the sunflower stood in the garden.

문장 A   문장 B

▌ FANBOYS 접속사 (딱풀, 연결체인)

문장 A   문장 B

FANBOYS : For   때문에
And   그리고
Nor   역시 아니다
But   그러나
Or   또는
Yet   그러나
So   그래서

For (때문에)	He's overweight, for he eats too many cakes and biscuits. 그는 비만이다. 그가 너무 많은 케익과 비스킷을 먹기 때문에.
And (그리고)	He baked cookies, and I made some tea. 그는 쿠키를 구었다, 그리고 나는 차를 만들었다.
Nor (역시 아니다)	He does not eat cake, nor does he eat biscuits. 그는 케익을 안 먹는다, 비스킷도 역시 안 먹는다.
But (그러나)	I eat cake, but I never eat biscuits. 나는 케익을 먹는다, 그러나 나는 비스킷은 절대 안 먹는다.
Or (또는)	Don't eat too many cakes, or you will be overweight. 너무 많은 케익을 먹지 마라, 안 그러면 비만이 될 것이다.
Yet (그런데도 여전히)	He's overweight, yet he continues to eat lots of cakes. 그는 비만이다, 그런데도 여전히 그는 계속 많은 케익을 먹는다.
So (그래서)	He was very hungry, so he ate all the cake. 그는 배가 아주 고팠다, 그래서 그는 모든 케익을 먹었다.

▌ when, why, how에 관한 정보(부수적인 정보)를 붙이는 접속사

이유 관련 : because, as, since, so that
시간 관련 : as soon as, until, before, whenever, when, while
기타 : if, although/even though, whereas, whether or not

접속사

문장 A   문장 B

when, why, how에 관한 정보

【이유】

because	Peter didn't go to work yesterday because he was ill.
(때문에)	Peter는 어제 일하러 안 갔다 왜냐하면 아팠기 때문에.
as	Peter didn't go to work yesterday as he was feeling unwell,
(때문에)	Peter는 어제 일하러 안 갔다 왜냐하면 몸 상태가 안 좋았기 때문에.
since	We should ask someone else since you are unable to answer.
(때문에)	우리는 다른 사람에게 물어봐야 해 왜냐하면 네가 대답을 못 하기 때문에.
so that	I'll lend you a map so that you can find the place more easily.
(하기 위해서)	내가 너에게 지도를 빌려 줄게 너가 더 쉽게 그 장소를 찾게 하기 위해서.

【시간】

as soon as	I'll call you as soon as I get home.
(하자마자)	내가 너에게 전화할 게 내가 집에 도착하자마자.
until	I'll wait until you arrive.
(할 때까지)	내가 기다릴게 네가 도착할 때까지.
before	Did he say anything before he left?
(하기 전에)	그가 뭐라도 말했니 그가 떠나기 전에?
after	She went for a long walk to relax after she finished her work,
(한 후에)	그녀는 오래 산책을 갔다 휴식을 취하려고 그녀의 일을 끝낸 후에.
whenever	The baby gets very grumpy whenever he's tired.
(할 때 마다)	그 아기는 짜증을 낸다 피곤할 때 마다.
when	Call me when you get home.
(할 때)	나한테 전화해 네가 집에 도착할 때.
while	They arrived while we were having dinner.
(하는 동안)	그들은 도착했다 우리가 저녁을 먹고 있는 동안에.

【기타 세부적 상황】

if (~라면)	We'll stay at home if it rains. 우리는 집에 머무를 거야 만약 비가 오면.
once (일단~하고 나면)	We will gather around the campfire to share stories once the sun sets. 우리는 캠프파이어에 둘러 앉아 이야기를 나눌 거다 일단 해가 지면.
unless (~하지 않으면)	I will not go outside unless it stops raining. 나는 밖에 안 갈 거야 비가 멈추지 않으면
although, even though (비록~일지라도)	They're happy, although/even though they're poor. 그들은 행복하다 비록 가난해도.
whereas, while (~인 반면)	Ellie is tall, whereas/ while her brother is short. 엘리는 키가 커 형/남동생은 작은 반면에.
whether or not (이든 아니든)	You are going to the dentist whether or not you like it. 넌 치과에 갈 거야 네가 좋든 싫든.

▌보충 설명

Q. 두 문장의 의미 관계를 접속사 말고 다른 말로 나타낼 수는 없을까?

◉ 각 빈칸에 들어갈 말을 아래 ⓐ~ⓔ중 고르시오.

(1) A new security system was installed. _____, extra guards were hired.

(2) He forgot his umbrella at home. _____, he decided to go for a walk in the rain.

(3) There aren't many jobs available. _____, companies receive hundreds of resumés for every opening.

(4) John excels in mathematics. _____, his sister is also a top performer in her science courses.

(5) She loves hot weather and enjoys spending time at the beach. _____, her sister prefers colder climates and skiing in the mountains.

연결 부사 (두 문장의 의미를 연결해 줌)	ⓐ	그러므로	Therefore, Therefore, Thus, Consequently, As a result, Hence, For this reason, Accordingly
	ⓑ	게다가	In addition, Additionally, Furthermore, Moreover, Besides
	ⓒ	그래도	However, Nevertheless, Nonetheless. Still, In spite of that,
	ⓓ	한편, 대조적으로	In contrast, On the contrary, On the other hand,
	ⓔ	비슷하게	Similarly, Likewise, In the same way,

☞ 정답: (1)ⓑ (2)ⓒ (3)ⓐ (4)ⓔ (5)ⓓ

접속사는 두 문장을 하나의 문장으로 통합시켜 두 문장의 의미 관계를 설명함.

(주어 + 동사 **접속사** 주어 + 동사.) ---> 문장 하나

한편, 연결 부사는 두 문장을 각각의 문장으로 유지하되 가운데 삽입되어 의미 관계를 설명함.

(주어 + 동사. **연결부사,** 주어 + 동사.) ---> 문장 두 개

다음 문장에서 접속사를 네모하고 문장의 의미를 설명하시오.

① We can play outside if it stops raining.

② I will call you as soon as I arrive home.

③ She likes to drink tea before she goes to bed.

④ I will go to the store when I finish my homework.

⑤ He is happy since he received a gift from his friend.

⑥ They went to the park even though it was raining.

⑦ She likes to eat ice cream whenever she feels sad.

⑧ He couldn't go to the party since he was feeling sick.

⑨ We chatted with our friends while we were waiting in line.

⑩ They studied hard because they wanted to get good grades.

다음 문장에서 접속사를 네모하고 문장의 의미를 설명하시오.

① I wonder whether it will rain tomorrow.

② I'm not sure if I can attend the party.

③ She asked if he had finished his work.

④ She asked me whether I had seen her keys.

⑤ They wondered if the train would be on time.

⑥ He asked me if I wanted to join him for lunch.

⑦ I don't know whether she will come to the party.

⑧ She asked him whether he wanted to go for a swim.

⑨ They wondered if the concert tickets were still available.

⑩ He couldn't remember whether he had finished his homework.

▌ 접속사(딱풀)가 있는 문장 구조

[한 눈에 딱! 나머지 접속사 묶음 문장 구조 알게 그림]

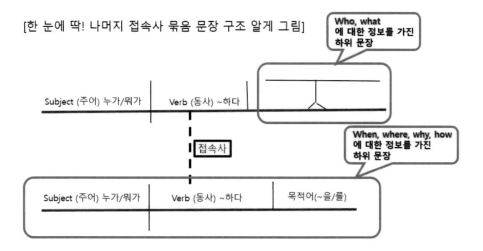

<예시 1> He's overweight, for he eats too many cakes.

     그는 비만이다. 그가 너무 많은 케익을 먹기 **때문에**.

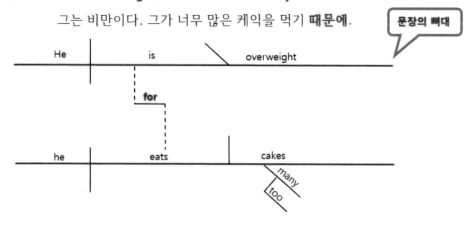

<예시 2> He does not eat cake, nor does he eat biscuits.

     그는 케익을 안 먹는다. 비스킷도 **역시 안** 먹는다.

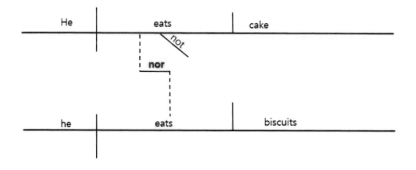

<예시 3> Don't eat too many cakes, or you will be overweight.

너무 많은 케익을 먹지 마라, 안 그러면 비만이 될 것이다.

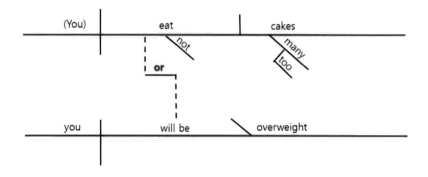

<예시 4> He was very hungry, so he ate all the cake.

그는 배가 아주 고팠다, 그래서 그는 모든 케익을 먹었다.

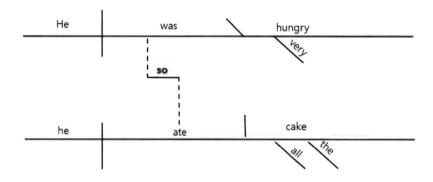

<예시 5> Peter didn't go to work yesterday because he was ill.

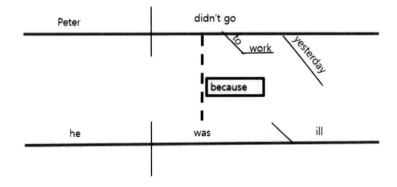

<예시 6> I don't know **whether** he ate all the cake.

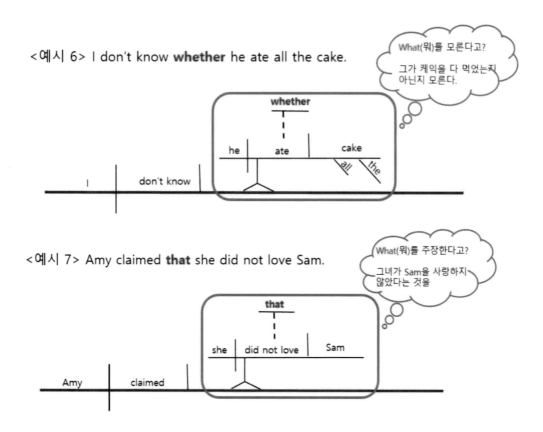

<예시 7> Amy claimed **that** she did not love Sam.

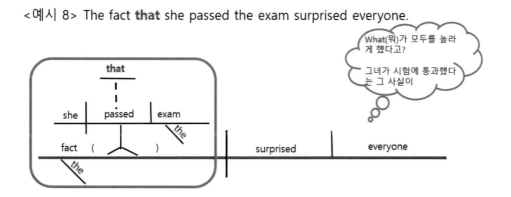

<예시 8> The fact **that** she passed the exam surprised everyone.

각 문장에서 접속사를 네모하고 문장을 선 그림(Diagramming)으로 그리시오.

① We can play outside if it stops raining.

② I will call you as soon as I arrive home.

③ She likes to drink tea before she goes to bed.

④ They went to the park even though it was raining.

⑤ I will go to the store when I finish my homework.

⑥ She likes to eat ice cream whenever she feels sad.

⑦ He is happy since he received a gift from his friend.

⑧ He couldn't go to the party since he was feeling sick.

⑨ We chatted with our friends while we were waiting in line.

⑩ They studied hard because they wanted to get good grades.

각 문장에서 접속사를 네모하고 문장을 선 그림(Diagramming)으로 그리시오.

① He asked me if I could attend the party.

② She asked if he had finished his work.

③ I wonder whether it will rain tomorrow.

④ She asked me whether I had seen her keys.

⑤ I don't know whether she will come to the party.

⑥ They wondered if the train would be on time.

⑦ He asked me if I wanted to join him for lunch.

⑧ She asked him whether he wanted to go for a swim.

⑨ They wondered if the concert tickets were still available.

⑩ He couldn't remember whether he had finished his homework.

각 문장에서 접속사를 네모하고 문장을 선 그림(Diagramming)으로 그리시오.

① I hope that you can join us for dinner.

② I believe that honesty is the best policy.

③ He mentioned that he had a meeting later.

④ She said that she would come to the party.

⑤ The belief that hard work pays off is true.

⑥ I know that he is passionate about his work.

⑦ I heard that they are planning a trip next month.

⑧ They made it clear that they would keep the secret.

⑨ The idea that honesty is the best policy is widely accepted.

⑩ It is true that education plays a crucial role in personal development.

▎관계대명사에 관한 핵심 사항

: 두 가지 요소(접속사, 명사)를 하나(관계대명사)로 압축함.

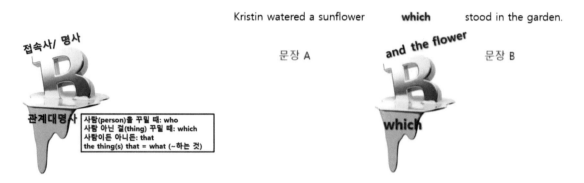

Kristin watered a sunflower **which** stood in the garden.

문장 A   and the flower   문장 B

접속사/ 명사

관계대명사

사람(person)을 꾸밀 때: who
사람 아닌 걸(thing) 꾸밀 때: which
사람이든 아니든: that
the thing(s) that = what (~하는 것)

which

▎ 관계대명사는 이럴 때 사용

❶ 앞 문장에 나온 사람(person)이나 사물(thing)이 구체적으로 어느 사람(which person) 또는 어느 것 (which thing)을 가르키는 지 꼭 짚어줘야 할 때 쓴다.

【필수 정보】이 부분이 없이는 Ann이 누군지 모르는 상황

Ann <u>who lives next door</u> is very friendly.

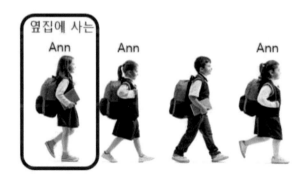

옆집에 사는
Ann   Ann   Ann

A: Ann is very friendly

B: Which Ann?

A: She lives next door.

B: Ah~ . Ann who lives next door is very friendly, right?

❷ 앞 문장에 나온 사람(person)이나 사물(thing)에 대해 추가 정보를 주고 싶을 때 쓴다.

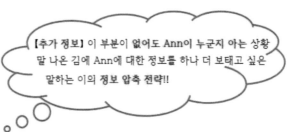

Ann **,** <u>who lives next door</u> **,** is very friendly.

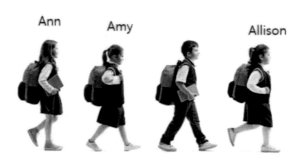

A: Ann is very friendly

B: Really?

A: She lives next door.

B: Ah~ . Ann, who lives next door, is very friendly, right?

다음 문장에서 관계사가 쓰인 절(작은 문장/안긴 문장)에 네모 하시오.

① The boy who is wearing a red hat is my brother.

② The shirt that I bought is too small for me.

③ The dog that barks loudly belongs to our neighbor.

④ The teacher whom I admire is very knowledgeable.

⑤ The movie that we watched last night was really exciting.

⑥ The person who called me on the phone was my friend.

⑦ The restaurant where we had dinner serves delicious food.

⑧ The book that I borrowed from the library is very interesting.

⑨ The house where I grew up is located in the countryside.

⑩ The day when Tom arrived from Korea was my birthday.

다음 문장에서 관계사가 쓰인 절 (작은 문장/안긴 문장)에 네모 하시오.

① My sister, who lives in London, is coming to visit us.

② John's car, which is red, is parked in the driveway.

③ Sarah's cat, which is named Max, loves to play with yarn.

④ My favorite book, which I read last summer, is a thrilling mystery.

⑤ The concert, which was held in the park, attracted a large crowd.

⑥ The Eiffel Tower, which is located in Paris, is a famous landmark.

⑦ The movie, which won several awards, is now available on DVD.

⑧ My uncle, who is a doctor, gave me some valuable medical advice.

⑨ The restaurant, which has a cozy atmosphere, is known for its delicious pasta.

⑩ The old house, which was built in the 1800s, has a lot of historical significance.

[한 눈에 딱! 관계대명사 묶음 문장 구조 알게 그림 1]

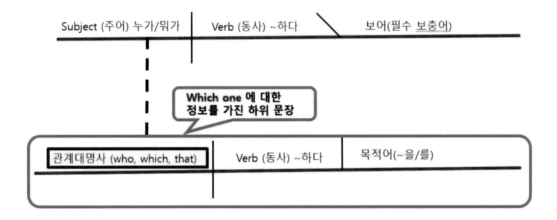

[한 눈에 딱! 관계대명사 묶음 문장 구조 알게 그림 2]

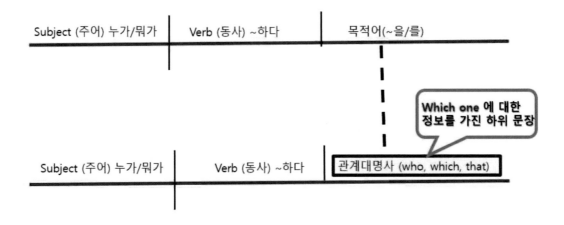

▌ 뼈대 잡기 연습 ① who

<예시 1> Ann who lives next door is very friendly.

        Ann (여러 Ann 중에 옆집에 사는)은/ 아주 친절하다 .

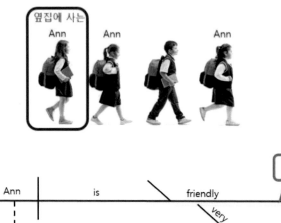

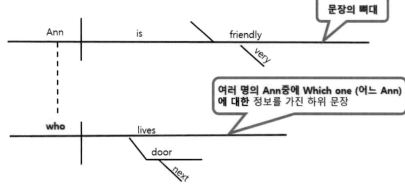

문장의 뼈대

여러 명의 Ann중에 Which one (어느 Ann)에 대한 정보를 가진 하위 문장

<예시 2> Ann, who lives next door, is very friendly.

        Ann (그리고 그 Ann은 옆집에 사는데,)은/ 아주 친절하다 .

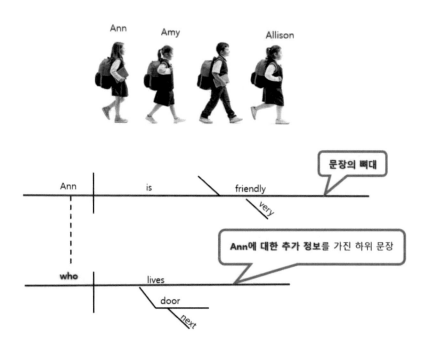

문장의 뼈대

Ann에 대한 추가 정보를 가진 하위 문장

<예시 3> Simon, **who had just started his diet**, woke up at midnight because he was hungry.

Simon (그리고 그 Simon은 이제 막 다이어트를 시작했는데,)이/ 잠에서 깼어 한밤중에 / 배가 고파서.

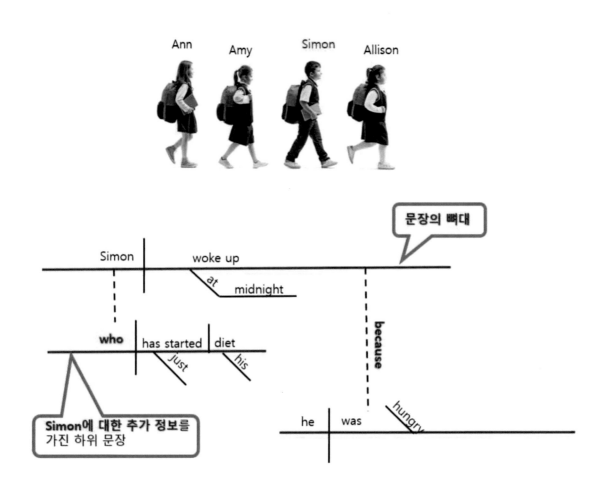

문장을 선 그림(Diagramming)으로 그리시오.

① The shirt that I bought is too small for me.

② The dog that barks loudly belongs to our neighbor.

③ The teacher whom I admire is very knowledgeable.

④ The boy who is wearing a red hat is my brother.

⑤ The car which is parked outside belongs to my neighbor.

⑥ The house that I purchased is located in the countryside.

⑦ The movie that we watched last night was really exciting.

⑧ The person who called me on the phone was my friend.

⑨ The restaurant which he recommended serves delicious food.

⑩ The book that I borrowed from the library is very interesting.

문장을 선 그림(Diagramming)으로 그리시오.

① John's car, which is red, is parked in the driveway.

② My sister, who lives in London, is coming to visit us.

③ Sarah's cat, which is named Max, loves to play with yarn.

④ My favorite book, which I read last summer, is a thrilling mystery.

⑤ The concert, which was held in the park, attracted a large crowd.

⑥ The Eiffel Tower, which is located in Paris, is a famous landmark.

⑦ The movie, which won several awards, is now available on DVD.

⑧ My uncle, who is a doctor, gave me some valuable medical advice.

⑨ The restaurant, which has a cozy atmosphere, is known for its delicious pasta.

⑩ The old house, which was built in the 1800s, has a lot of historical significance.

▌ 뼈대 잡기 연습 ② what

<예시 4> I can't hear what you are saying.

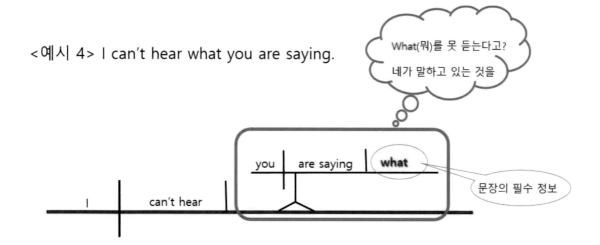

문장을 선 그림(Diagramming)으로 그리시오.

① I believe what he told me.

② Show me what you bought.

③ He'll give you what you need.

④ What he did was morally wrong.

⑤ Tell me what you want for dinner.

⑥ I can't find what I'm looking for.

⑦ I want to know what he thinks.

⑧ Can you describe what you saw?

⑨ What you said is absolutely right.

⑩ I don't understand what you're saying.

문장을 선 그림(Diagramming)으로 그리시오.

① She showed me what she had found.

② He explained to me what had happened.

③ Show me what you've been working on lately.

④ She showed me what true friendship means.

⑤ Explain to me what you want for your birthday.

⑥ He described to me what he saw during your trip.

⑦ Share with me what inspired you to pursue this career.

⑧ What he built was a remarkable piece of engineering.

⑨ What they chose to wear was inappropriate for the formal event.

⑩ Inform me what your preferred choice is for the upcoming event.

문장을 선 그림(Diagramming)으로 그리시오.

① Tell me what your name is.

② I don't know where she lives.

③ I can't predict what he will tell me.

④ Ask him how he will go to the party.

⑤ Show me what you will wear to the party.

⑥ Ask him when he will go to the meeting.

⑦ Can you tell me why he will go to the meeting.

⑧ What the rumor is about does not matter at all.

⑨ Whether we travel by boat or not is up to you.

⑩ How you express your anger affects others' feelings.

◉ 관계대명사 'what'과 의문사 'what'
관계대명사 'what'과 의문사 'what'의 문장 구조는 똑같아요.
굳이 구별하려 애쓰지 않아도 됩니다.
관계대명사 'what'은 '~하는 것'으로 의문사 'what'은 '무엇'으로 우리말로는 구별해서
번역하지만 영어로는 그 구별이 무의미합니다.

▌ 뼈대 잡기 연습 ③ -1 when, where, why, how

<예시 5> The day when Tom arrived from London was my birthday.

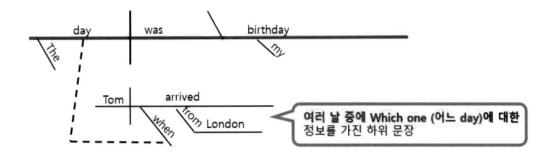

여러 날 중에 Which one (어느 day)에 대한 정보를 가진 하위 문장

문장을 선 그림(Diagramming)으로 그리시오.

① This is the place where we first met.

② Do you remember the day when we first met?

③ I visited the town where I spent my childhood.

④ Let me show you the way the system functions.

⑤ I found a quiet spot where I could read my book.

⑥ The time when the sun sets is my favorite part of the day.

⑦ He explained the reason why he was late to the meeting.

⑧ Can you tell me the reason why the project was postponed?

⑨ The period when she lived abroad shaped her perspective.

⑩ I'll demonstrate to you the way the software operates.

▌ 뼈대 잡기 연습 ③ -2 when, where, why, how

<예시 6> I wonder when he will go to the meeting.

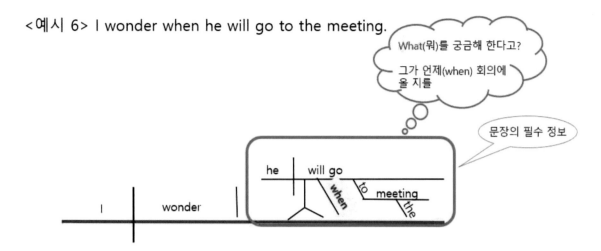

문장을 선 그림(Diagramming)**으로 그리시오.**

① She asked me when the next train would arrive.

② Tell me where you found that interesting article.

③ I wonder why he decided to change his career.

④ He questioned why the company chose to relocate.

⑤ They asked us when the event was scheduled to start.

⑥ Do you know when the new software will be released?

⑦ Could you explain where you got those fantastic shoes?

⑧ Tell us where you plan to spend your summer vacation.

⑨ He inquired why the project time-line was extended.

⑩ Please share with me how you achieved such remarkable success.

◉ 'when, where, why, how'가 관계부사와 의문사로 쓰일 때 각각의 문장 구조는 달라요. 각 쓰임 별 문장 구조의 차이점을 잘 살펴보세요.

▌ 문장 가성비 최고로 높이는 방법 : 준동사 (현재분사: -ing) 활용하기

【 영어 고수들의 문장 가성비 높이는 방법 】
 : 낱개의 두 문장을 접속사로 묶기

Kristin watered a sunflower, __and__ the sunflower stood in the garden.

Kristin watered a sunflower   , and   the sunflower stood in the garden.

문장 A   문장 B

【 영어 고수들의 문장 가성비 더 높이는 방법 】
 : 관계대명사(접속사 + 대명사 압축) 사용

Kristin watered a sunflower __which__ stood in the garden.

Kristin watered a sunflower   __which__   stood in the garden.

문장 A   문장 B

and the flower
B
which

【 영어 고수들의 문장 가성비 가장 높이는 방법 】
  : 준동사(verbals: −ing) 사용

Kristin watered a sunflower <u>standing</u> in the garden.

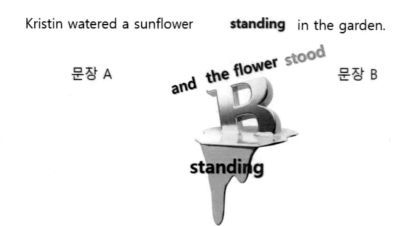

▮ 세 가지 상황별 연습

<상황 1> Kristin은 해바라기에 물을 주었다 그리고 그 해바라기는 정원에 있다.

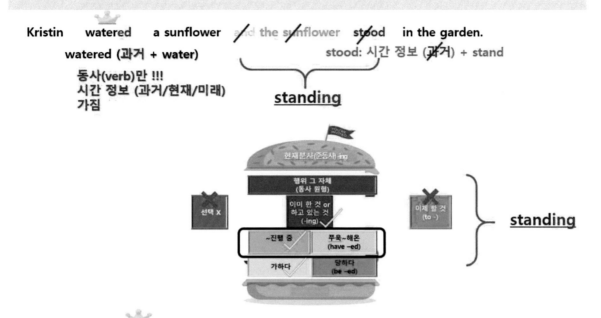

Kristin   watered   a sunflower   ~~and the sunflower~~   stood   in the garden.

watered (과거 + water)

stood: 시간 정보 (~~과거~~) + stand

동사(verb)만 !!!
시간 정보 (과거/현재/미래)
가짐

standing

standing

Kristin watered a sunflower   standing   in the garden.

<상황 2> Kristin이 레모네이드 한 잔을 마셨다, 해바라기에 물을 주고 난 후.

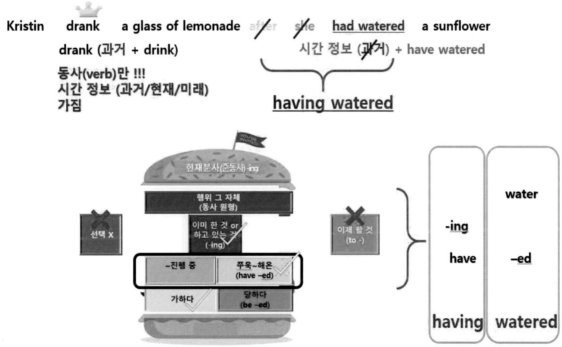

Kristin   drank   a glass of lemonade   ~~after~~   ~~she~~   had watered   a sunflower

drank (과거 + drink)

시간 정보 (~~과거~~) + have watered

동사(verb)만 !!!
시간 정보 (과거/현재/미래)
가짐

having watered

-ing   water
have   -ed
having   watered

Kristin drank a glass of lemonade, having watered a sunflower.

<상황 3> 해바라기 ('물줌'을 쭈욱 당해 온)가 꽃을 피웠다(blossomed).

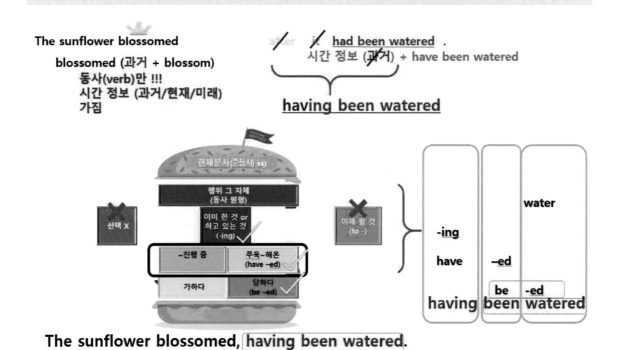

The sunflower blossomed

blossomed (과거 + blossom)
동사(verb)만 !!!
시간 정보 (과거/현재/미래)
가짐

after it had been watered .
시간 정보 (과거) + have been watered

having been watered

The sunflower blossomed, having been watered.

다음 문장을 압축할 때 괄호 안 단어를 알맞게 바꾸시오.

① She smiled and she hugged the panting dog.

= _____ **(smile),** she hugged the panting dog.

웃으면서, 그녀는 숨을 헉헉거리는 개를 안았다.

② After he had been shaken, he walked away from the wrecked car.

= _____**(shake),** he walked away from the wrecked car.

큰 충격을 받고, 그는 사고당한 차에서 걸어 나왔다.

③ As he whistled to himself, he walked down the road.

= _____ **(whistle)** to himself, he walked down the road.

휘파람을 불며, 그는 길 아래로 걸어 내려갔다.

④ She dropped the gun and put her hands in the air.

= _____ **(drop)** the gun, she put her hands in the air.

총을 떨어트리며, 그녀는 두 손을 공중으로 들어 올렸다.

⑤ He put on his coat and left the house.

= _____ **(put)** on his coat, he left the house.

코트를 입으며, 그는 집을 나섰다.

⑥ Because he was poor, he didn't spend much on clothes.

= _____ (be) poor, he didn't spend much on clothes.

가난했기 때문에, 그는 옷에 돈을 많이 안 썼다.

⑦ Because he knew that his mother was coming, he cleaned the flat.

= _____ (know) that his mother was coming, he cleaned the flat.

그의 엄마가 온다는 사실을 알았기 때문에, 그는 아파트를 청소했다.

⑧ He whispered because he thought his brother was still asleep.

= He whispered, _____(think) his brother was still asleep.

남동생이 여전히 자고 있다고 생각했기 때문에, 그는 속삭였다.

⑨ After they had been informed, they immediately took action to resolve the issue.

= _____ (inform), they immediately took action to resolve the issue.

정보를 얻고 나서, 그들은 당장 문제를 해결하기 위해 조치를 취했다.

⑩ After he had been praised, he felt a sense of accomplishment.

= _____(praise) , he felt a sense of accomplishment.

칭찬을 받고, 그는 성취감을 느꼈다.

▌ '동사원형 ing'에 관해 기억해야 할 딱 두 가지

1. 콤마(,) 동사원형ing : ~하며

[그림 1 : 콤마(,) '동사 원형ing']

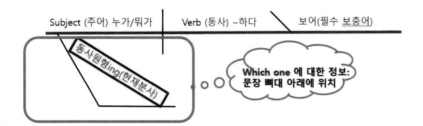

<예시 1> Kristin watered a sunflower **, standing** in the garden.

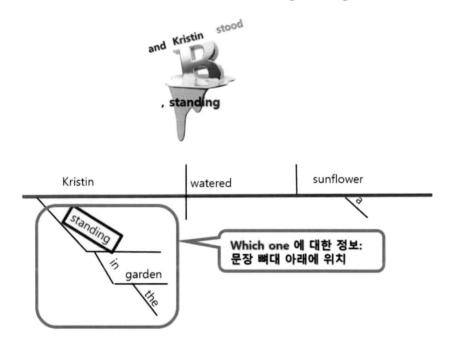

문장을 선 그림(Diagramming)으로 그리시오.

① We cleaned the house, humming a tune.

② We cooked dinner, laughing and chatting.

③ He fixed the car, listening to the radio.

④ He wrote a letter, sitting at the kitchen table.

⑤ They played soccer, cheering on their team.

⑥ Emily painted a picture, sitting at her desk.

⑦ They built a sandcastle, playing on the beach.

⑧ I took a photograph, capturing the sunset.

⑨ The cat chased a mouse, running through the room.

⑩ She baked a cake, singing along to her favorite song.

2. 콤마 없는 동사원형ing : ~하고 있는

[그림 2 : 콤마(,) 없는 '동사원형ing']

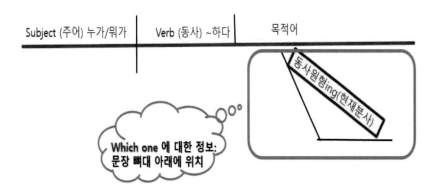

<예시 2> Kristin watered the flower **standing** in the garden.

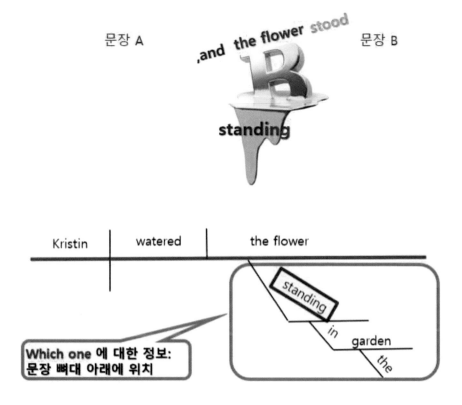

문장을 선 그림(Diagramming)**으로 그리시오.**

① He found a coin lying on the sidewalk.

② He caught a fish swimming in the river.

③ I saw a rainbow stretching across the sky.

④ They heard a bird singing from the treetop.

⑤ She noticed a spider crawling up the wall.

⑥ Sarah painted a picture hanging on the wall.

⑦ They observed a squirrel leaping from tree to tree.

⑧ The cat chased a mouse hiding behind the couch.

⑨ The child watched a butterfly fluttering among the flowers.

⑩ We witnessed a shooting star moving quickly through the night.

▌참고

'동사원형 ing'의 또 다른 기능 - : ~하는 것

[그림 3 : 콤마(,) 없는 동사원형ing]

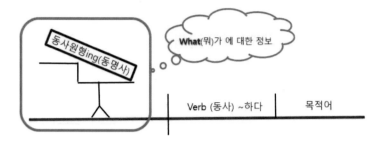

<예시 3> Drinking coffee at midnight causes sleep problems.

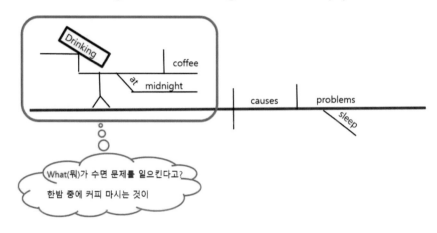

문장을 선 그림(Diagramming)으로 그리시오.

① I like painting pictures.

② They enjoy listening to music.

③ Running every morning keeps me fit.

④ We appreciate receiving thoughtful gifts.

⑤ Practicing yoga regularly relaxes the mind.

⑥ Exploring new cultures broadens our horizons.

⑦ Baking delicious cookies brings joy to the family.

⑧ Learning new vocabulary words improves language skills.

⑨ Volunteering at the local shelter is a fulfilling experience.

⑩ Traveling to different countries exposes us to diverse perspectives.

Day 13. 상상 말하기 (가정법)

▌Q. 왜 가정법이 애초에 생겼을까?

◉ 엉뚱하지만 유쾌한 상상을 하고 싶어서.

◉ 과거에 대한 후회, 아쉬움, 현재에 대한 불평, 불만과 같은 감정을 나누고 싶어서.

▌Q. 왜 영어는 상상해서 말하기를 할 때 동사의 시제를 그렇게 철저히 구분할까?

◉ 우리말은 어떤 일의 실현 가능성 정도는 상황, 문맥에서 파악한다고 보기 때문에 동사 시제에 별 의미를 두지 않음.

◉ 영어는 상황이나 문맥에 상관없이 문장 안에 모든 정보가 정확히 표현되어야 한다고 봄. 상상해서 말하기(가정법)를 할 때 동사의 시제에 실현 가능성 정도를 반드시 표시해야 함. 동사의 시제가 의미 전달에 아주 결정적임.

(A) If I won the lottery, I would travel around.
   아주 실현 가능성이 없는 그저 엉뚱한 상상
   (복권을 사지도 않고 한 말일 가능성이 높다.)

(B) If I win the lottery, I will travel around.
   실현 가능성이 다소 있는 그럴듯한 상상
   (복권을 이미 사고 번호를 맞추기 일보 직전에 할 수 있는 말이다.)

● 가능성 정도도 동사 형태로 "구별"함.

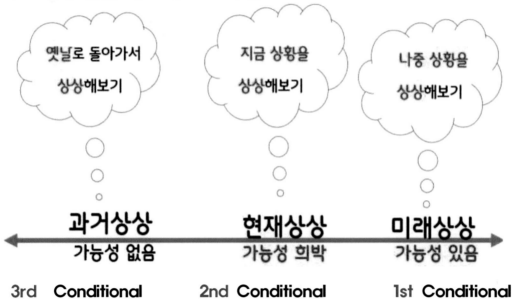

옛날로 돌아가서 상상해보기

지금 상황을 상상해보기

나중 상황을 상상해보기

과거상상
가능성 없음

현재상상
가능성 희박

미래상상
가능성 있음

3rd Conditional   2nd Conditional   1st Conditional

▮ Q. 상상해서 말할 때 동사 형태는 어떻게 다를까?

: 상상해서 말할 때의 동사 형태는 현실을 말할 때와 다르다.

● 현실 시간 아래처럼 "구별"함.

● 상상임을 표시하기 위해 "바로 이전 시제"에서 동사 형태 빌려 옴.

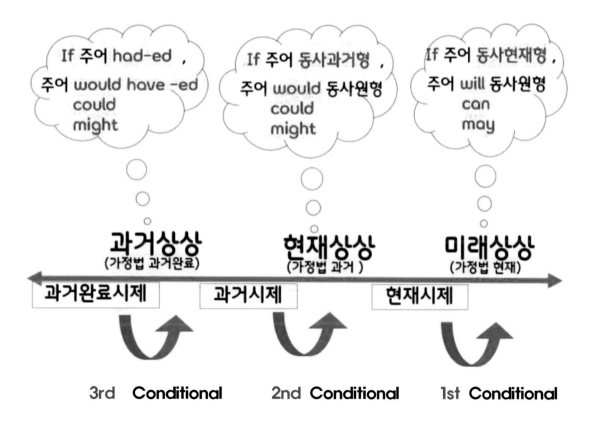

▌예시

예를 들어 '내 10억이 있다면'이라는 상상을 각 시간별로 아래와 같이 말할 수 있다.

1. 과거 상황으로 돌아가 상상할 경우 : If I **had had** 1 billion won then, I **would have bought** it.
   (과거 완료/대과거 시제 빌려 옴)

2. 지금 상황에서 상상할 경우　　　: If I **had** 1 billion won now, I **would buy** it.
   (과거 시제 빌려옴)

3. 미래로 가서 상상할 경우　　　: If I **have** 1 billion won later, I **will buy** it.
   (현재 시제 빌려옴)

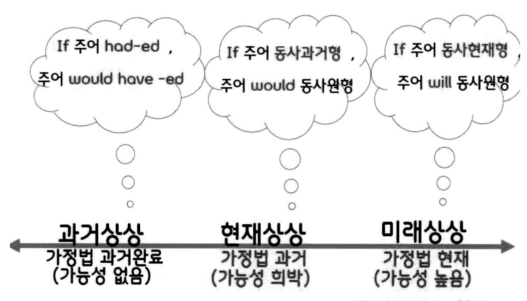

◉ 입으로 익혀보자

If I had run faster, I would have been the winner.

(내가 더 빨리 달렸었더라면, 우승자가 될 수 있었는데)

▌가정법 핵심 파악 3단계

Step 1. 가정법 핵심 사항 다시 한번 이해하기!!

★ 상황과 실현 가능성 정도에 따라 세 가지 다른 "상상해서 말하기"를 씀.
  - 과거 상상: 과거에 이미 일어난 상황을 뒤집어 상상해 봄-실현 가능성이 없음.
  - 현재 상상: 현재 일어나고 있는 상황을 뒤집어 상상해 봄-실현 가능성이 거의 없음.
  - 미래 상상: 미래에 일어나지 않은 상황을 예상하며 상상해 봄-실현 가능성이 다소 있음.

!! 핵심 !!

● 가능성 정도도 동사 형태로 "구별"함.

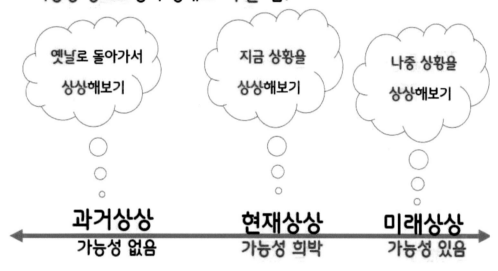

▌상황에 따라 골라 쓰기

A: Well, If you **cook** Rameyon, I **will have** it. (네가 라면 끓여주면, 내가 먹을 텐데...)

B: OK. I will cook it for you. (알겠어. 내가 끓여줄게.)

--> 라면을 끓여줄 가능성은 상당히 높다. 그래서 미래 상상하기 즉 **가정법 현재**를 사용한다.

상황 2. (한국에 있는 A와 미국에 있는 B의 문자 대화)

A: I miss Korean food so much. I enjoyed the Rameyon you cooked for me.

(난 한국 음식 많이 그립다. 네가 끓여준 라면 참 맛있었는데.)

If you **cooked** Rameyon, I **would have** it. (네가 라면 끓여주면, 내가 먹을 텐데...)

B: Did you enjoy it that much? Thanks anyway. (그렇게 맛있었어? 아무튼 고마워.)

---> 라면을 끓여줄 가능성은 거의 없다. 그래서 현재 상상하기 즉 **가정법 과거**를 사용한다.

▌말하는 의도와 태도에 따라 골라 쓰기

'Will you..?'와 'Would you...?' 중 왜 'Would you..?'가 더 공손한 표현일까?

상황 1. (친구끼리 대화)

A: **Will** you open the window (if you **can**)? (네가 할 수 있으면, 창문 열어줄 거니?)

B: Sure. (물론이지)

--> **상대가 창문을 열어 줄 가능성이 높다고 생각**하며 말함.

　(가정법 현재 사용)

상황 2. (낯선 사람한테 부탁하는 대화)

A: **Would** you open the window (if you **could**)?

　(당신이 혹시라도 하실 수 있으시면, 창문 열어 주실 수 있나요?

B: Sure. (물론이죠.)

--> **상대가 창문을 열어 줄 가능성이 낮지만 그럼에도 부탁**한다는 뉘앙스로 말함.

　(가정법 과거 사용)

▌"상상"임을 표시해야 함.

실제 상황에 대한 이야기가 아니라 **상상 속 이야기일 때는** "이전 시제를 빌려와서" 상상임을 표시해야 함.

!! 핵심 !!

● 상상임을 표시하기 위해 "바로 이전 시제"에서 동사 형태 빌려 옴.

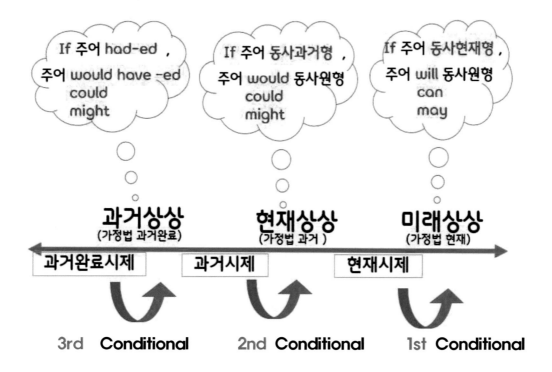

가정법 기본 패턴 딱 세 개 만 통째 암기!!

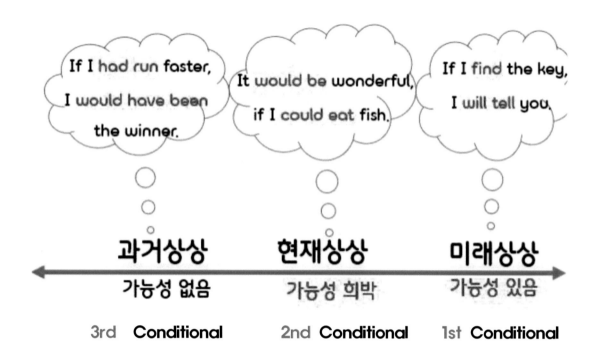

Step 3. **다양한 문장 구경하고 내 걸로 만들기!!**

다음은 원어민들이 실제로 쓰는 가정법 문장들입니다. 한번 확인해 보시고 나중에 쓸 것 같은 문장을 입으로 여러 번 읽으면서 익혀보세요. '상상해서 말하기(가정법)'를 자기 상황에 적용해서 말해 보세요.

▌미래 상상 표현(가정법 현재 시제 사용) 1st Conditional

다가올 미래 일로 가능성 높을 때 쓸 수 있는 말이다.

① I will answer if he calls me.

(내가 받을 거야 만약 그가 전화하면 나에게.)

② Jenny will buy this dress if it's on sale.

(제니는 이 드레스 살거야, 만약 할인한다면.)

③ I will attend the wedding if I'm invited.

(내가 결혼식에 참석할 거야 만약 초대받는다면.)

④ If I study really hard, I'll ace this test.

(만약 진짜 열심히 하면, 내가 이 시험에 일등 할 거야.)

⑤ He will be late if the traffic is heavy.

(그는 늦을 거야 만약 차가 많이 막히면.)

⑥ If the weather is good, our crops will flourish.

(날씨가 좋으면, 수확물이 잘 자랄거야.)

⑦ My sister will cry if she watches this movie.

(내 여동생을 울 거야 만약 이 영화를 본다면.)

⑧ She will get the job if she impresses the interviewer.

(그녀는 그 직업을 얻을거야 만약 면접관에게 좋은 인상을 남긴다면.)

⑨ If the kids eat too much candy, they'll have a stomachache.

(만약 아이들이 사탕을 너무 많이 먹으며, 그들은 배가 아플 거야.)

⑩ You will succeed in college if you're diligent in your studies.

(너는 대학교에서 성공할 거야 만약 공부를 부지런히 하면.)

▌현재 상상 표현 (가정법 과거시제 사용) 2nd Conditional

현재 일이지만 **가능성 희박한 상황일 때** 쓸 수 있다.

① I would answer if he called.
 (내가 받을 텐데 만약 그가 전화한다면.)

② If I were rich, I'd never work again.
 (내가 부자라면, 다시는 일 안 할 텐데.)

③ I would faint if I ever met Brad Pitt.
 (내가 기절할 거야, 내가 Brad Pitt을 만난다면.)

④ If it snowed, we would build a snowman.
 (지금 눈이 온다면, 우리가 눈사람을 만들 텐데.)

⑤ If he were taller, he would play basketball.
 (그가 더 키가 크다면, 그가 농구를 할 텐데.)

⑥ If I won the lottery, I would buy a new car.
 (내가 로또에 당첨된다면, 새 차를 하나 살 텐데.)

⑦ She would quit her job if she found a better one.
 (그녀는 그녀의 직업을 그만둘 텐데 만약 더 나은 직업을 찾는다면.)

⑧ Harry would help you move if he knew where you lived.
 (해리가 네가 이사하는 걸 도울 텐데 만약 그가 안다면 어디에 네가 사는 지.)

⑨ If I had a magic wand, I would make all your dreams come true.
 (마법 봉이 있다면, 내가 너의 모든 꿈을 다 실현 시켜줄 텐데.)

⑩ If you resolved to be diligent in your studies, you would succeed in college.
 (만약 공부를 부지런히 한다고 결심한다면, 너는 대학교에서 성공할 텐데.)

▌과거 상상 표현 (가정법 과거 완료시제 사용) 3rd Conditional

이미 지난 과거 일이라 실현 가능성 없지만 한번 상상해 볼 때 쓸 수 있다.

① I would have helped if I'd known you were in trouble.

(내가 도와줬을 텐데 만약 내가 알았더라면 너가 힘든 상황이라는 것을.)

② If Bonnie had studied, she would have passed the test.

(만약 Bonnie 가 공부했더라면, 그녀가 시험에 통과했을 텐데.)

③ If he had asked her out, she would have said yes.

(만약 그가 그녀에게 데이트 신청을 했었더라면, 그녀가 수락했을 텐데.)

④ If it hadn't rained, we would have gone to the beach.

(만약 비가 안 왔더라면, 우리가 해변에 갔었을 텐데.)

⑤ If I had seen the warning, I would have avoided the accident.

(만약 내가 그 경고를 봤었더라면, 그 사과를 피할 수 있었을 텐데.)

⑥ They would have succeeded if they had worked together.

(그들이 성공 했을텐데 만약 그들이 같이 일을 했었더라면.)

⑦ Your dog would have bitten my dog if he hadn't been on a leash.

(너의 개가 내 개를 물었을거야 만약 그가 목줄을 하지 않았었더라면.)

⑧ My family wouldn't have bought the house if they had seen the broken pipes.

(나의 가족은 그 집을 안 샀을 거야 만약 부서진 파이프를 봤었더라면.)

⑨ If she had arrived five minutes earlier, she would have seen the whole show.

(만약 그녀가 도착했다면 5분 일찍, 그녀는 쇼 전체를 다 봤을 텐데.)

⑩ Pearl wouldn't have made that comment if she knew her brother was listening.

(Pearl은 그런 말을 안 했을 텐데 만약 그녀가 알았다면 그녀의 남동생이 듣고 있다는 것을.)

아래 괄호 속 단어 중 알맞은 것을 고르시오.

If she finishes her work early, she ⓐ(will join/join) us for the movie tonight. We're all excited about the film, and we've saved a seat for her just in case. If her boss doesn't give her any last-minute tasks, she'll have the opportunity to relax and enjoy the movie with us. We've heard great reviews about it, and we hope she can make it. If she ⓑ(will decide/decides) to come, we'll grab some popcorn and make the evening a fun and memorable one. However, if something unexpected ⓒ(will come up/comes up), we understand and will fill her in on all the exciting parts later.

아래 괄호 속 단어 중 알맞은 것을 고르시오.

If the train ⓐ(will arrive/arrives) on time, I'll make it to the meeting without any issues. I've planned my route carefully, and if everything goes smoothly, I should be able to present the project updates to the team. I've prepared the necessary documents and slides, so if the presentation ⓑ(will go/goes) well, it will lead to positive feedback from the higher-ups.

아래 괄호 속 단어 중 알맞은 것을 고르시오.

If I ⓐ(attended/had attended) that music festival last year, I could have seen some of my favorite bands perform live. I remember debating whether to buy tickets, and if I had gone, I ⓑ(may/might) have witnessed memorable performances and shared the excitement with fellow music enthusiasts. I ⓒ(had danced/could have danced) to the tunes of my beloved artists and created lasting memories. Unfortunately, circumstances prevented me from going, and I missed out on what could have been an unforgettable weekend.

아래 괄호 속 단어 중 알맞은 것을 고르시오.

If I ⓐ(will finish/finish) my chores early, I'll join you for the game tonight. I've been eagerly waiting for this match, and if I manage to complete all my tasks, ⓑ(I'll have/ I have) the time to relax and enjoy the game without any worries. If our team ⓒ(will play/plays) well and secures a victory, it will definitely boost our spirits. I'll bring some snacks to share, and if the atmosphere in the stadium is energetic, it'll be an unforgettable experience. However, if I get held up with my responsibilities, I'll have to miss the game, but I'll be cheering our team on from home.

아래 괄호 속 단어 중 알맞은 것을 고르시오.

"If I ⓐ(have/**had**) more free time, I would travel to all the places I've dreamed of visiting. I've always wanted to explore different countries and immerse myself in new cultures. If I didn't have work commitments and other responsibilities, I ⓑ(will/**would**) book a flight and set off on exciting adventures. I ⓒ(will/**would**) visit historic landmarks, try exotic cuisines, and meet people from all walks of life. If I ⓓ(can/**could**) choose any destination, I would probably start with a tour of Europe, taking in the rich history and stunning architecture. However, since my current schedule ⓔ(were/**is**) busy, I'll have to settle for occasional weekend getaways to nearby places for now.

아래 괄호 속 단어 중 알맞은 것을 고르시오.

If I ⓐ(am/**were**) a skilled musician, I would compose beautiful melodies that touch people's hearts. I've always admired the way music can evoke emotions and connect people. If I had the talent to play multiple instruments and write intricate compositions, I ⓑ(will/**would**) spend my time crafting songs that inspire and uplift. I would collaborate with other artists and create harmonious pieces that resonate with a wide audience. Even though I ⓒ(didn't/**don't**) have that level of musical ability, I ⓓ(could/**can**) still appreciate and enjoy the work of talented musicians around the world.

아래 괄호 속 단어 중 알맞은 것을 고르시오.

If I ⓐ**(live/lived)** in a warmer climate, I ⓑ**(would/will)** spend more time outdoors and engage in various outdoor activities. I've often thought about how different my lifestyle would be if I ⓒ**(reside/resided)** in a place with milder winters and longer summers. If the weather ⓓ**(is/were)** consistently pleasant, I ⓔ**(would/will)** go hiking, have picnics, and maybe even learn to surf. I'd enjoy the most of the natural beauty around me and embrace an active lifestyle. However, since I currently ⓕ**(lived/live)** in a colder region, I ⓖ**(would try/try)** to make the best of the seasons by enjoying winter sports and cozy indoor activities.

아래 괄호 속 단어 중 알맞은 것을 고르시오.

If I ⓐ**(have/had)** the chance to meet my favorite author, I would ask them about their writing process and the inspiration behind their stories. Reading their books has always transported me to different worlds, and if I ⓑ**(can sit/could sit)** down with them, I would express my admiration for their work. I would inquire about their characters' development and how they create such immersive settings. If we ⓒ**(could/can)** have a conversation, it ⓓ**(will/would)** be a dream come true. Yet, even if I never get the opportunity, their writing will continue to inspire my own creativity and love for storytelling.

아래 괄호 속 단어 중 알맞은 것을 고르시오.

If I ⓐ**(studied/had studied)** architecture in college, I might have been designing innovative buildings today. Looking back, I often wonder how my life would have unfolded if I ⓑ**(chose/had chosen)** a different path. If I had pursued my interest in architecture, I might have been working on projects that shape city skylines and blend functionality with aesthetic appeal. I ⓒ**(could have been/can be)** part of teams that create sustainable structures and redefine urban spaces. However, my decision to study economics led me down a different road. While I don't regret my choices, I can't help but imagine the alternate reality where I followed my architectural aspirations.

아래 괄호 속 단어 중 알맞은 것을 고르시오.

If I ⓐ**(took/had taken)** that job offer abroad, I might have experienced a completely different culture and lifestyle. When the opportunity arose to work in a foreign country, I considered the possibilities. If I ⓑ**(had accepted/accepted)** the offer, I ⓒ**(may/might)** have learned a new language, made international friends, and gained insights into diverse ways of living. I could have explored unfamiliar cities and immersed myself in a global community. However, I decided to stay in my current job for personal reasons. While I'll never know what those experiences could have been like, I'm content with the life I've built here.

Conclusion

20년 경력의 중등 현직 영어 교사이지만 학교 내신 영어 시험 기간만큼은 대한민국 영어 교육에 대해 무기력감을 느낍니다. 영어 교사들의 K-영문법(한국에서만 통하는 한국 사람들만 알고 원어민들은 모르는 영어 문법)에 대한 지나친 집착이 고스란히 아이들의 한숨으로 이어지는 기간이기 때문입니다. 거대한 산과 같은 K-영문법에 대한 맹신은 저 혼자의 힘으로 도저히 바꿀 수 없습니다.

대한민국 아이들은 유년 시절 영어 다르고 초등 영어 다르고 중학 영어 다르고 고등 영어 다른 그런 지그재그 영어 교육을 받는다고 해도 틀린 말이 아닙니다. 매번 학교급이 바뀔 때마다 틀어지는 영어 교육의 방향 때문에 웬만한 의지가 아니고서는 끝까지 영어를 즐겁게 배울 학습자는 없습니다. 영어라면 질색하며 수능 영어를 끝으로 영어에 손을 떼게 만드는 게 우리의 현실입니다.

과연 유치원 때부터 대학교 졸업할 때까지, 그리고 사회인으로 살아가면서까지 모두 통하는 영어는 없을까요? 그 질문에 대한 해답은 영어를 익히는 방식에서 찾을 수 있다고 생각합니다. 우리도 원어민들처럼 영어를 익히면 그들처럼 학교급에 상관없이 일관된 영어 능력을 키울 수 있습니다. 원어민식 영어 공부법의 가장 대표적인 것이 바로 문장 선 그림 그리기입니다. 문장 선 그림 그리기(Sentence Diagramming)는 길고 복잡한 구조의 문장을 시각적으로 나타내어 문장의 뼈대를 파악하는 방법입니다. 문장 선 그림 그리기는 초등부터 고등에 이르기까지 영어 원어민 아이들에게 필수 문법 교육으로 자리 잡고 있습니다.

우리나라 사람은 우리나라 영문법으로 공부해야 하고 원어민들은 원어민식 영문법 교육이 따로 있다고 생각하시나요? 대한민국의 영어 교육은 수능 영어로 귀결된다고 해도 과언이 아닙니다. 대부분 수능 영어의 지문은 미국의 유명한 대학교 전공 서적에서 발췌하며 수능 영어가 평가하는 핵심 역량은 바로 문해력입니다. 결국 우리나라 영어 학습자들도 원어민 학습자들처럼 영어로 된 전공 서적을 읽어낼 수 있어야 합니다. 그럼에도 불구하고 왜 군이 우리나라 학습자들은 K-영문법이라는 엉뚱한 관문을 통과해야 비로소 그런 문해력을 익힐 수 있다고 다들 믿는 것일까요? 학부모도 현장의 교사들도 중학교 입학과 동시에 그런 K-영문법에 왜 그렇게 집중하는지 모르겠습니다. 언제까지 영어 원어민들도 알지 못하는 K-영문법을 우리 아이들에게 답습시켜야만 할까요? 과연 그것이 대학교에서 읽게 될 전공 서적을 읽어내는 데 필수 도구일까요? 추상적이고 논리적인 영어 지문, 그것도 복잡하고 긴 문장으로 이루어진 그 글을 술술 읽어내기 위해 K-영문법은 과연 얼마나 효과가 있을까요?

새로운 것에 대한 거부증은 인간의 생존 본능입니다. 하지만 땅만 보고 한숨 쉬며 왜 배우는지 이유도 모르는 그런 K-영문법의 굴레를 쓰며 몇십 년 같은 실수를 답습할 수는 없습니다. 이제 그 굴레에서 벗어나 잠시 시선을 돌려 이 책을 바라봐 주셨으면 합니다. <한국식 영문법 말고 원어민식 그림 영문법>과 워크북은 영어 문장을 영어 문장으로 받아들이며 영어적 사고의 흐름에 익숙해질 수 있는 그런 진짜 영문법을 익히기 위한 최소한의 도구입니다.